oOo

Oh, Vulgar Wind

A

SYMPATHETIC

OVERVIEW

OF THE

COMMON

FART

Oh, Vulgar Wind

Munroe Scott

Munroe Scott

CULTURE CONCEPTS
Publishers
Toronto Canada

ISBN: 0-921472-47-1

CANADIAN CATALOGUING IN PUBLICATION DATA

Scott, Munroe, 1927-

Oh, vulgar wind: a sympathetic overview of the common fart

Includes bibliographical references.

ISBN: 0-921472-47-1

1. Flatulence. 2. Flatulence – Humor. I. Title.

RC862.F55S36 1994 612.3 C94-930212-0

Culture Concepts books are available at special discounts for
bulk purchases as premiums, or for fund-raising, sales promotions
or educational use. Please contact us at:

CULTURE CONCEPTS INC.

5 Darlingbrook Crescent

Toronto Ontario Canada M9A 3H4

Telephone: 416 231-1692

Fax: 416 237-1832

Illustrations Iryna Molodecky

Design: Robert MacDonald / MediaClones Inc.

Printed and bound in Canada

CONTENTS

FOREWIND

There are those who, when they see the subject matter of this modest work, will relegate it to the humour section, the novelty stand, or the waste basket. Certainly the subject of flatulence is one that is usually consigned to either low comedy or limbo. This work is different. *Oh, Vulgar Wind* is a serious work in intent, if not always in treatment.

Being flatulent is the price we all pay for being a part of the animal kingdom. Some people pay a heavier price than others. As vegetarian and high fibre diets become more popular, flatulence inevitably soars. This continually inflating situation requires society and individuals to make adjustments that are dietary, linguistic, psychological, and even cultural.

Readers of a genteel frame of mind are assured that they are in good company in pursuing this subject. Flatulence has become popular fodder for stand-up comics who are excellent barometers of public pressures but whose humour, alas, is too often devoid of wit. The problem of flatulence arises more and more frequently in casual references in ordinary conversation as well as TV talk shows and radio interviews. And for many years some members of the medical profession have been calling for greater attention to be paid to the whole gaseous problem.

In her *Guide to Personal Health*, popular food writer Jane Brody says,

Whether it merely causes private pain or is the source of significant public embarrassment, intestinal gas is a vexing problem for millions of people. Although not yet a topic for cocktail party conversation, the recent

fibre revolution and the growing reliance on vegetable sources of protein have helped to make intestinal gas a matter of widespread concern.[1]

Dr. Ted Boadway, Director of Health Policy for Canada's Ontario Medical Association says, "... we must become a bit more comfortable talking about farting ... an entirely normal physiologic reaction to a better diet."[2]

One reason our subject is not yet a topic for polite conversation is that the English language, magnificent though that vehicle is, has developed no suitable vocabulary. Taboos surrounding flatulence have not only inhibited conversation, they seem to have inhibited scientific study. In 1978 the *American Family Physician* warned that the gas problem was not only serious but very common.[3] The same year two contributors to *Medical Clinics of North America* bewailed,

Although symptoms thought to be due to 'too much gas' are among the most frequently encountered in medical practice, there has been little scientific study of this problem. For this reason, physicians seldom deal rationally with excessive gas ...[4]

Two years later one of the authors of the above complaint reported more hopefully in *The New England Journal of Medicine*: "Although intestinal gas is still relatively unexplored, interest in this topic appears to be increasing."[5]

About the same time, the author and his associate had this to say:

In general, it appears that complaints of excessive passage of flatus are more closely related to psychosocial factors than the actual quantity of gas excreted.[6]

If the real problem lies in the social strictures that create psychological problems and if this book helps to soften social censure by broadening perspective then it will have performed a timely and useful service. With that objective in mind, the following is not merely a layperson's overview of medical progress but also a brief survey of the history, the language, the facts and the myths that surround the common fart.

Throughout the body of this work, surnumber references are used to document the sourcs of scientific information and the works from which quotes or specific knowledge have been drawn. Readers can consult the detailed references under the Notes section for further reading pleasure. These are also intended to reassure readers that the author is presenting views based on history, on literature and on current scientific research – a view that is, of course, filtered through the author's perception.

MS

Balsam Lake, 1994

ACKNOWLEDGMENTS

With sincere appreciation to the many readers who
offered helpful comments and especially to editors
Glenda Lewe and Ian Van Heyst.
Special thanks for encouragement to
Annette Vance Dorey, Dr. Vladimir Vuksan,
Brenda Hutchinson, and to consulting dietitians
Barbara Engle, Janice Schmeltzer
and Beth Duviner.

Oh, vulgar wind that blows where'er it pleases;
That fans the stools of wise men, fools,
And kings as rich as Croesus;
That pipes its way with merry note
Through prelate, parson, priest and pope,
And rests but never ceases.

Fragment

CHAPTER
ONE

The Outcast

Disgrace and misdemeanor
The Queen's amnesia
The setting's the sin
Lack of verbal riches
Verbal flatuosity
Clarity with gentility
Enlightenment and liberation
Naming the unspeakable
Speaking the unspeakable
"...with fart-healt thanks..."
Intrepid explosion of trail blazing
The unbidden and never welcome presence
Wafting onward and upward

CHAPTER
ONE

The Outcast

One day, about 400 years ago, the Earl of Oxford was being presented to Her Majesty Queen Elizabeth the First of England. The Earl, like all supplicants, no doubt fondly hoped the Queen would take special note of him; that she would observe something original about his dress, or appreciate something striking in the calibre of his wit. Indeed, anything that would help his most powerful of sovereigns to recall him with kindness and clarity should the occasion ever arise that she felt called upon to dispense royal favours.

oOo

Disgrace and misdemeanor

Oxford had dined simply but well that day. Alas, too well. As he moved toward the foot of the throne his large colon filled with intestinal gases. As he dropped to stockinged knee, plumed hat in deferential hand, the muscular contortions of the courtly genuflection caused said gases to be expelled from his rectum to the accompaniment of a loud and sudden report not unlike the firing of a small cannon.

So great was milord's humiliation that, without more ado, he rose to his feet, backed slowly and humbly from the regal presence, and sent himself into voluntary exile.

oOo

The Queen's amnesia

Seven years later, the Earl of Oxford, hoping that his monumental indiscretion had blown over, returned to the court of the "faery Queen". As no courtier mentioned or even hinted at his earlier and lamentable loss of control, he felt confident his impropriety was no longer remembered as once again he knelt before his sovereign.

Good Queen Bess greated him amiably and graciously, but loudly proclaimed, "My Lord, I had forgot the fart."

The account of the Earl of Oxford's ordeal was preserved for posterity by a 17th century biographer, John Aubrey,[1] and the story of the poor nobleman's disgrace strikes the same sympathetic chords today as it did at the time of telling. His was the ultimate social fart. It created embarrassment for others, humiliation for himself, and through following ages, merriment for many.

Milord's misdemeanour was surely as natural an act as is possible for the human animal to perform. He spoke no ill, caused no harm, and meant no disrespect. Yet so great was his shame that he instantly administered his own punishment. So unforgettable was that explosive climax that, years later, the memory of it had to be annulled by a royal declaration of amnesia. So noisily flew the flatus that the humour of the moment would be shared for ever afterwards.

Milord's fart owes its fame, and indeed much of its hilarity, to its timing. For all we know he may have released one, inadvertantly of course, earlier in the day after consuming a simple meal of coarse bread and local cheese. But if anyone heard they took no note. He may have laid one across the saddle as he mounted to canter leisurely to report at the palace, but no groom would have reacted. Indeed, it could have been attributed to the horse.

oOo

The setting's the sin

It becomes self evident that although there may be a variation in quality between one fart and another, it is the setting that's the sin. And the sin, in the proper setting, induces both shame and laughter. Paradoxically, the laughter itself, becoming contagious, can produce more involuntary sin. Fart induced laughter is, short of death, the greatest of levellers.*

What is this perfectly natural and often unavoidable act that stimulates, simultaneously, two such profound and yet contradictory human emotions as shame and laughter?

oOo

Lack of verbal riches

Why is it that such a universally common thing as a touch of flatulence is represented in the English language, that storehouse of verbal riches, by so few words? "Fart" has almost no synonyms.

---

*The levelling power of the fart is hereby acknowledged in verse:

> There once was a knight called Arteur
> Renowned for hoity hauteur
> Until once at the table
> He laughed at a fable –
> Becoming a famous farteur.

The few approximations that exist will be exhausted in these introductory pages (with the exception of "crepitate" which we will save for an erudite chapter dealing with classifications).

"Borborygmus" usually refers to the inner abdominal rumblings of travelling gas rather than to its sudden rectal release. "Flatus" is a correct term for rectally expelled air and "flatulence" names the condition, but even here there is no universal agreement as to the precise meaning of flatulence. Dr. R. Hecker, writing as Director of Gastroenterology at the Royal Adelaide Hospital in Australia, defines flatulence as "the term used by patients or doctors to describe belching, the passage of flatus, excess borborygmi or just a feeling of abdominal fullness and distension."[2]

oOo

Verbal flatuosity

If the passing of flatus can be equated with belching (or burping) then the language is far too imprecise. Nor is it fair to the fart. Belch and burp are both good homespun words that pass muster even in genteel conversation but when it comes to a lower passing there is no single word to replace fart. There is certainly no other verb.

It is conceivable but not desirable, that a verb could be created from flatus. "To flatulate" comes to mind and will, one hopes, be forgotten. "To flat" is no better. A noun, "flatulogram," is, unfortunately, already in the literature as the name of a clinical chart recording a patient's daily passing of wind.[3] "Flatology" is becoming an accepted term, although it is not yet a subspeciality of medicine. Its practitioners are "flatologists."[4] Such words are all very well for the scientific community that has an aversion to plain language but the uninitiated can see at a glance that such concoctions lead to a flatuosity in language that is the antithesis of the good fellow fart.

oOo

Clarity with gentility

In attempting to achieve clarity while maintaining gentility some members of the medical research community use "downwind" as a fart substitute.[5] This fabrication is not only coy but like flatulence, is lamentably lacking a verb. The authors of scientific papers cope with the missing verb by cumbersome references to "passing flatus." The best we nonprofessionals can do to maintain verbal decorum is to speak of "breaking wind" or "passing wind." It becomes apparent that we are communicating creatures whose bodies are afflicted with a universal action for which the English language has only one verb, "to fart," and that verb is socially proscribed.

oOo

Enlightenment and liberation

We pride ourselves on living in an uninhibited era but when it comes to flatulence our prissiness would astonish Good Queen Bess who, by definition, spoke the Queen's English and apparently had no antipathy to the fart as a word. Today, we who are supposedly enlightened and liberated consistently allow the language of courteous discourse to be shackled by the dictates of the intelligentsia.

In 1950, *The Concise Oxford Dictionary* said the word "fart" was indecent but offered no suitable replacement. *The New*

Century Dictionary (1953) and *The New Webster Encyclopedic Dictionary of the English Language* (1967) both omitted the word altogether, thereby leaving us, orally at least, mute. In 1967, a saucy little Collier reference work entitled *Webster's Unafraid Dictionary* claimed to treat 5000 words both defiantly and definitively but was not defiant enough to define a fart. The same year, *The Dictionary of American Slang* declared the word to be taboo, thereby putting a total interdiction on its use. In 1989 the second edition of *The Oxford English Dictionary* said the word was not in decent use and then devoted almost seven inches of fine print column space to following the fart's trail from 1386 into the 20th century. Recent editions of other distinguished dictionaries label the word as vulgar.

oOo

Naming the unspeakable

It is difficult to attribute vulgarity to a word that has managed so valiantly to embody, as it were, a universal essence, but the act represented by the word is indeed vulgar, often to the point of being sublime – alas, another paradox!

The very vulgarity of both word and deed make it difficult to approach either one in a philosophical frame of mind. Even choosing a title for a modest text such as this proved a formidable task, it not being our intent to antagonize sensitive readers. *The Passing Wind* was eliminated as being uncomfortably facetious. *The Wayward Wind*, being the title of a song, would have been appropriate but might have violated copyright thus adding another transgression to the fart's dossier. *The Unspeakable Thing* came to mind, for reasons that will become apparent shortly, but one can hardly call something unspeakable and then write a book about it.

Oh, Vulgar Wind is, however, an honest summation of the subject matter and carries no whiff of either sophistication or exclusiveness, two affectations that have never afflicted the fart. The phrase has the added advantage of being found in a fragment of verse, thereby giving it cultural tone.*

oOo

Speaking the unspeakable

When one inspects the origin of the word "fart" one is struck by a universality and tenacity that is truly remarkable. Most words change with time, their origins being almost hidden in multitudinous mutations. Not so with fart. Nor are its origins attributable to a single language. One is tempted to blame the Angles and Saxons (or the Dutch) for all four-letter vulgarities in the English language, but although their ancient life styles would suggest a crapulence equal to that of any other, in this case they can claim no proprietorship.

Whether it be Middle English, *ferten*, Old High German, *ferzan*, Old Norwegian, *freta*, or even Greek or Sanskrit, a commonality of origin can not only be seen but heard. It is a commonality that has drifted down through the ages unashamed and unadulterated.

---

*Honesty compels me to explain the term "fragment." I liked the title but needed a verse to support it and so wrote three verses and threw two away, hence "fragment." This confession should be safe, hidden as it is in a footnote.

oOo

"...with fart-healt thanks..."

A few valiant efforts are being made to give the fart its rightful place in our language. In 1978 the *New England Journal of Medicine* published a letter that read as follows:

To the Editor:

This letter is to make it official. The word fart was used factually, without embarrassment at 13:10 hours on Wednesday, May 17, in Lecture Room B, University Hospital, during a lecture to the second-year medical class on "Gaseousness". I was encouraged to use the term by the recent correspondence on the matter in the Journal. I am essentially a religious, God-fearing man, an avoider of obscenities and a lover of the English language. On due reflection I was persuaded of the intrinsic value of this word and of its non-offensiveness. The students have been encouraged to use it freely where clinically appropriate. Not unnaturally, there were a few titters; indeed it would even be appropriate to say there were even a few guffaws at first. But once the word had been used a few times, it came to sound natural and as unremarkable as any other suitable clinical term.

I hope that all other clinicians, men of honour and upright standing, will follow this lead. A spark has been struck; a torch has been lit. Let it shine forth and illumine the dark recesses of what has hitherto been that unspeakable thing.

I am, acknowledging the encouragement of the Journal, with fart healt thanks,

W.C.Watson, MD [6]

Canadian readers can take pride in the knowledge that Dr. Watson was writing from Victoria Hospital in London, Ontario, and that his call of liberation may not have gone unheeded. By

1985 one finds Dr. N.W. Read of the Department of Physiology of the University of Sheffield in England, using the word unabashedly as a substitute for flatulence and wind.[7]

oOo

Intrepid explosion of trail blazing

In spite of trail blazing by intrepid clinicians, one cannot write a popular book on the universal fart without being sensitive to the pitfalls of undue vulgarity. Always at the writer's elbow are the Siamese twins of scatological and bathroom humour. These we will try to avoid. We have already demonstrated that there is no avoidance of the irrepressible pun and *double entendre*. Scientific literature dealing with flatulence is permeated by both.

Dr. D. F. Altman of the Department of Medicine, University of California, writing in a prestigious journal, says that it is "an area in which our understanding has literally exploded in the last several years."[8] The South African co-authors of "Air flow Studies in Excessive Flatulence" cannot resist prophesying "a more harmonic" future.[9] Dr. E. R. W. Fox, describing a case history of flatulence for *The Western Journal of Medicine* yields to temptation by saying that it was a matter of "innermost concern."[10]

oOo

The unbidden and never welcome presence

It is tempting to say that the purpose here is to rehabilitate the fart, but rehabilitation implies the restoration of a good reputation and former privileges. The fart has never enjoyed either. One is also tempted, in the pride of authorship, to claim the intention of illuminating and elevating one's subject but in this case the subject can do that all by itself.

Nor does the valiant fart need a herald. It has announced its own presence among kings, khans, peasants, slaves and tyrants. It speaks out in the company of prime ministers, diplomats, beauty queens, labourers, school children and babes. It has enthusiastically entered the space age and journeys with the cosmonauts, as we shall see in the next chapter. It comes unbidden and is never welcome. It is, to adopt Danny Kaye's description of a saxophone, an ill wind that nobody blows good. It is obvious that what the fart needs is simply sympathetic understanding.

It is to be hoped that this introductory chapter has created some empathy for the word itself and some sympathy for its plight as an outcast in both speech and society.

oOo

Wafting onward and upward

We have empathized with the Earl, bemoaned our English language lack of verbal riches, noted with pleasure and pride the intrepid clinicians' verbal trail blazing and solemnly underlined the pressing need for sympathetic understanding and the social rehabilitation of an unwelcome but ever-present little fellow.

Next we shall explore Nature's Human Power Plant, examining what goes down and what goes on in the human flatus factory and meet non-celestial Blue Angels.

CHAPTER
TWO

Why the Wind Blows

A mad wizard's wish list
From humanoid to human
Nature's power plant
What goes down ...
The human flatus factory
High altitude propulsion
Life threatening explosions
Non-celestial Blue Angels
The foul miscreant
Wafting backward

CHAPTER
TWO

Why the Wind Blows

In these days when the vile emissions of an industrial society are destroying inland seas, searing the forests, polluting the oceans and rending the very canopy of Earth, we do well to pause to admire the smaller 'industrial emission' that is the common fart.

Let us conjure up images of human-like robots. They are commonplace in the world of science fiction. No self respecting interstellar space traveller would want to be without one. It is one thing, however, to create a verbal or cinematic illusion of an android and quite another to make one that actually functions.

oOo

A mad wizard's wish list

Consider the challenge facing design engineers attempting to create a robot to emulate the human body. Detailing the specifications alone would put their brains into overload.

The android will need, first and foremost, a computer brain capable of storing and accessing 70 years or so of experience and programming. It must be able to assess and compare information and make intuitive cross references that will be accurate even when defying logic. The computer will also control all mechanical functions from second to second during its entire existence.

The robot must be rustproof, waterproof, self propelled, amphibious and even submersible. It must be able to walk, run, jump, and climb.

If the designers' imaginations have not already short-circuited they can further ponder the specifications calling for built-in sensors that can perceive the scuffle of a mouse and yet withstand a nearby clap of thunder. Other detection devices must be able to read air temperatures and wind direction, analyze odours, and identify materials by texture. Additional sensors, when unobstructed, must incorporate automatic range finders to calculate and evaluate the speed and position of objects and be able to identify the presence of planets and suns billions of kilometers away.

We might continue with our mad wizard's wish list of fantastic requirements, such as tool-like appendages, and a circulation pump that will run nonstop for many decades. But returning to our discussion of emissions (our specific interest here), the robot must create its own energy by burning self-gathered, self-processed and self-stoked organic fuels in a self-contained power plant.

Even if we fantasize that our engineers are able to build such an android, imagine the final size and weight of the contraption! Consider, above all, the nature of the fuel used in the robot's internal power plant and the resultant slag heaps of solid waste and billowing clouds of gaseous waste.

oOo

From humanoid to human

Fortunately, Nature has already developed a design that is both compact and efficient, especially in energy intake, absorption and emissions. In North America the average male version weighs in at about 81 kilograms. A human male 19 to 24 years requires a daily fuel intake of about 3000 calories, while the female functions well on about 2100 calories.[1] A person can extract the required calories from about 725 grams of suitable organic fuels. In a process called digestion, mechanical agitation and chemical acid baths reduce the fuel to only a few grams of daily waste materials. The volume of waste gas created varies from one to three litres.

So compact and versatile are these extraordinary organic machines called humans, that they are able to battle their way into stores to buy consumer goods; to destroy entire ecosystems in order to produce those goods; to squash themselves into crowded subway cars; to immolate themselves on battle fields; to devise intricate rules and organizations to protect themselves from their own follies; to explore the universe and their own souls; to jump, scream and applaud in the noise, heat, and strobing light of a rock concert; to write mind-expanding literature and compose soul-moving music; to search for the beginning of Life and to seek to unravel the mystery of Death. Punctuating all this almost-universal activity is the ubiquitous, universal, random yet reticent release of a little gas.

Those emissions are a minuscule by-product of a miracle of industrial efficiency. Yet the act of disposing of that by-product is prohibited in polite society and the name for the act is (as we have seen in our previous discussion) virtually ostracized from the language. In attempting to suppress the fart we deny one of Nature's most remarkable engineering achievements.

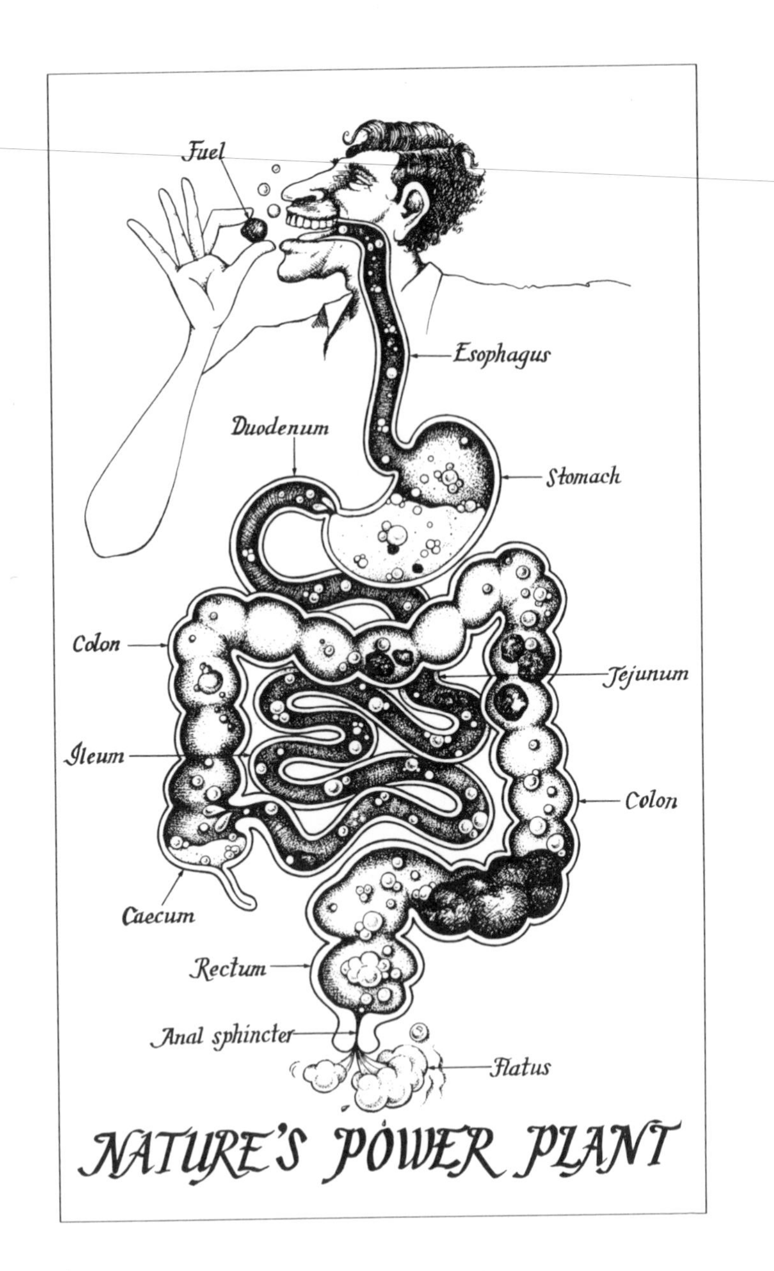
Fuel
Esophagus
Duodenum
Stomach
Colon
Jejunum
Ileum
Colon
Caecum
Rectum
Anal sphincter
Flatus
NATURE'S POWER PLANT

oOo

Nature's power plant

Let us follow the fuel through Nature's power plant and concentrate our attention upon the phenomenon of waste gas.

We can see that this is an open system.Quite simply, fuel goes in at one end, waste goes out at the other end. The fuel intake travels straight down the Esophagus and into the Stomach. The movement of fuel then follows a slight uphill climb into the Duodenum, takes a plunge into the Jejunum, and enters a tortuous route that leads into the Ileum and continues on into the Caecum. In the Colon, it progresses upward, across and down with a fine disregard for anything having to do with gravity. Finally it bottoms out in the Rectum, and is temporarily retained in its place by the Anal Sphincter muscle.

It is not our intent to explain the method by which organic fuel is turned into the energy that powers this amazing human contraption. Nor is it our purpose to explain the intricate mechanisms that move fuel and waste through the human power plant. But it is our intent to sniff out those vapourous trails of waste management.

oOo

What goes down...

As organic fuel (meat and potatoes, pizza and beer, soup and sandwiches etc.) is swallowed, a certain amount of air is taken down with it. Many people have a nervous habit of swallowing excessive air with every mouthful of food. But even a drink of water can be accompanied by twice as much air as water. As well, the food itself contains gas. Indeed, one fifth of the volume of an apple is said to be composed of gases[2] (which may have legendary repercussions as we shall see in the next chapter).

Whether it is swallowed or inhaled, most of this gas is expelled by means of what the medical profession like to call "eructation" and what you and I are more inclined to call a "burp" or a "belch." Major dictionaries have recognized the rather violent belch but until recently failed to acknowledge the more discreet burp.

Thanks to the mighty belch and the gentle burp only some of the gas that comes down is actually retained. A portion of this gas is nitrogen. Some researchers ignore swallowed air as a source of later emissions while others feel that it is highly significant, like Dr. Hecker who writes, "As this gas will pass from the stomach to the colon within 20 minutes, swallowed air is the commonest cause of excess flatus."[3] It seems likely too, that oral motions caused by ill-fitting false teeth and gum chewing increase the amount of air swallowed.

Flatologists who monitor human gaseous emissions watch for the presence of nitrogen and say that increased air intake can increase the nitrogen emitted by as much as 70%.[4] It seems, therefore, that the Nitrogen Fart is merely a belch that quietly sank, or a burp that slowly inverted. But that is not all. A small quantity of oxygen is also swallowed and expelled but as with the swallowed nitrogen, it is merely a vagrant traveller passing through; a meandering tourist, not a locally nurtured native.

oOo

The human flatus factory

Of more interest are the gases actually created in the human flatus factory. Acids combine with bicarbonate and produce carbon dioxide. This production takes place over a period of several hours following the major fuel stoking event commonly known as a hearty meal and can result in the production of 3000 millilitres of carbon dioxide. This is enough carbon dioxide to fill three litre-size pop bottles.

The chemical reactions that produce carbon dioxide are greatly assisted by the presence of complex carbohydrates which are found in numerous foods and especially in beans. Beans will be heard from later on but in the meantime we can think of the primary carbon dioxide fart as a Bean Fart.

But let us not blame everything on the bean. Fat may be another culprit. Thirty grams of fat may liberate, through the digestive process, as much as three litres of carbon dioxide.[5]

Usually more carbon dioxide is manufactured than actually makes it to an external exit. In this whole elaborate fuel burning process, all kinds of energizing substances are constantly moving through the digestive system into the bloodstream. Some of the waste carbon dioxide is absorbed internally in this way too.

oOo

High altitude propulsion

Normally, the pressure in the intestines is greater than the pressure in the bloodstream, thus forcing some carbon dioxide into the bloodstream which transports it to the lungs where it is expelled into the outer air. At high altitudes, however, there is a greatly reduced internal pressure. Gases then move *from* the bloodstream into the digestive system. Under such conditions the quantity of gas that must eventually be expelled is greatly increased.

At least one study [6] claims that the fart of a high altitude mountaineer is about 80% carbon dioxide and that most of it is generated outside the digestive system. It is intriguing indeed to consider who might have carried out such research, and how. It also conjures up images of intrepid climbers making the final assault on the crest of Everest assisted by an invisible but powerful form of jet propulsion. The Carbon Dioxide High Altitude Fart is, for the same reasons, said to be a robust companion of the astronauts. One can only assume that such reports have been censored by eMission Control.

Certainly the unconstrainable fart is a constant stowaway in all high technology spacecraft where, in the rarified scientific atmosphere, it masquerades under the acronym HAFE (High Altitude Flatus Expulsion).[7] Pondering the implications of having HAFE as a companion in the close-quartered communal life of the astronauts tempers our reverential admiration with compassion.

In the meantime, however, this does elevate the carbon dioxide flatus to greater levels than a mere old-fashioned Bean Fart. It is the Astrofart. This Vulgar Wind is every bit as complex, resilient and mobile as the human body that produces it.

oOo

Life threatening explosions

Bacterial action also produces hydrogen which is a highly explosive gas. Without the presence of bacteria no hydrogen is created nor is the gas present in any quantity during a fast. Readers with a practical turn of mind will understand that herein lies one of the many good reasons surgeons insist that patients avoid food and drink hours before certain operations.

Hydrogen present in the digestive system, when ignited by electrocautery, has been known to cause life threatening explosions.[8] We hasten to say that patients who follow their doctor's instructions need not fear such 'blastic' surgery.

Hydrogen production is greatly enhanced by fermentable substances such as sugar. Fortunately most sugars do not get as far as the intestines but some sugars from complex carbohydrates are not readily digested and so may linger in the company of bacteria where they join together in fermentation.

Such fermentation may add to the production of hydrogen. One of the fuels likely to contain the required complex carbohydrates is, alas, beans. It becomes obvious that a Bean Fart (a.k.a. Astrofart), being either carbon dioxide or hydrogen or both, is a sophisticated fart that may indeed merit the elevated position it holds in mythology, folk humour, science and the arts.

oOo

Non-celestial Blue Angels

There is yet another gas that is created by bacteria. It is methane. Methane is familiar to most of us as swamp gas that bubbles up from the murky bottom of a marsh. In this form it has been mistaken as being everything from ghosts to extra-terrestrial Unidentified Flying Objects.

It also erupts from volcanoes. There are those who claim it is methane rising in gigantic bubbles from the floor of the Atlantic's "Bermuda Triangle" that is responsible for the abrupt disappearance of ships. The water beneath them suddenly being replaced by a gigantic methane bubble, the ships are said to plunge to the depths. Then as the gas floats skyward, weightless, offering no support to wings, it is also said to cause the sudden downfall of aircraft. Methane may quite rightly be thought of as Nature's Fart.

Exotic methane becomes even more intriguing when considered in terms of the human fart. It does not explode like hydrogen, but it does burn.

Generations of school boys know this and delightedly demonstrate to their peers by holding lighted matches near the seat of emission, igniting blue flames not unlike the blast from a blowtorch. These flares are sometimes called "Blue Angels".

Readers with an experimental turn of mind may be tempted to hurry off to ignite a Blue Angel. In theory this could lead to a universal conflagration. Studies [9] in the United States, however, suggest that only one out of every three adult Americans produces significant quantities of methane and, amazingly enough, the ability tends to run in families. No corroborative data is available from the well-lit regions of Canada or elsewhere but one can assume that private research will continue to illuminate the subject.

oOo

The foul miscreant

We have seen then, that the waste gases from the fuel that supplies the remarkable human power plant are oxygen, nitrogen, carbon dioxide, hydrogen and methane. They are all weightless, colourless and odourless. Singly or in unison they are the components of the common fart.[10]

First hand experience, however, proves that the fart is not always odourless. Those that announce their prescence in this obtrusive way owe their noxious qualities to traces of very light vapours sometimes produced by bacteria. The most obnoxious of these vapours is hydrogen sulphide. The Hydrogen Sulphide Fart is undesireable indeed and will at no time be eulogized here. It is a miscreant whose presence has taken away from the standing of the more reputable, forthright and wholly exemplary odourless fart. Its victims, however, both producer and recipient, merit much sympathy and we will consider ways to deflate the wretched fellow.

Regardless of what type of waste gas is accumulated, it must eventually collect and await periodic release. The remarkable release mechanism can be triggered automatically or voluntarily depending upon the needs and sensitivities of the host body – and sometimes of the external social conditions. But inevitably and irretrievably, the gas must escape.

oOo

Wafting backward

It is no wonder, given the many releases a day from every human in the world, that some of those emissions should still reverberate through the annals of history. Let us then leave physiology and peer into the bowels of the past.

CHAPTER
THREE

Where the Wind Has Blown

Of apples and fragrant airs
Pythagorus prohibits beans
Hippocrates blesses wind in lower regions
Rome fears death by restraint
St. Augustine praises those who sing backward
Fear of the unexpelled weakens inhibitions
Chaucer lets fly
Rabelais' life-unifying air
Montaigne laments life-threatening release
Swift explains the blast that puts out fires
Balzac's ambition for a most natural thing
Twain's thundergusting prodigy
Le Petomane's astonishing 'singing' repertoire
Ecclesiastical, dinner and stage punctuations
A Canadian lover's agonizing deflation
Beans assault the screen
Assimilating the wind

CHAPTER
THREE

Where the Wind Has Blown

In a slim volume such as this, one cannot chronicle events back to the beginnings of time, and yet our subject, being a part of Nature is natural, and as old as all animal kind. For now, we will confine our musings and investigations to the human era and to the human animal.

oOo

Of apples and fragrant airs

We know that the newborn baby begins to produce waste gases within 30 minutes of birth. Is it not reasonable to assume that even Adam and Eve must have gone into production with similar alacrity, especially when we recall that one fifth of the volume of an apple is said to be composed of gases?[1] Our subject must have frolicked amidst the fragrant airs of the Garden of Eden itself. Let us, however, leap across the eons of evolution (or the centuries after Creation, depending upon our perspective) until we come to a time in the ancient Mediterranean world about 500 years before the birth of Christ.

oOo

Pythagorus prohibits beans

In Italy, when that territory was still a colony of Greece, Pythagorus, the scholar, was born on the Aegean Island of Samos. We remember Pythagorus as the mathematician and geometrician who proved that the square of the hypotenuse of a right-angle triangle is equal to the sum of the squares of the other two sides. He himself was so impressed by his deduction that he rushed out and sacrificed a goat.

If not exactly a philosopher, Pythagorus was certainly a mystic and his followers believed that he was divinely inspired. After his death they established Pythagorean brotherhoods that were monastic in lifestyle and purpose. The Pythagorean brothers maintained that friends held all things in common. One is tempted to assume that it was the master's insight into the aromatic truth of this statement that caused him to bid his followers: "*A fabis abstinetes,*" which admonition, being translated, tells us, "*Eat no beans!*"[2]

When we ponder the implications of the Pythagorean exhortation (which should be taught alongside his more famous theorem), we come to the conclusion that the Vulgar Wind, even amongst a brotherhood, was not considered genteel. The taboo was already in place. Even so, it was challenged within a century by Hippocrates.

oOo

Hippocrates blesses wind in lower regions

About 400 BC, on the small Aegean Island of Kos, Hippocrates practised his medical arts. Although descended from a line of Greek priest-physicians who healed their patients by means of charms, mumbo-jumbo and invocations to the gods, Hippocrates preferred a more scientific approach. He discarded the craft's priestly superstitions and relied on his own observations. He was a pioneer in public health, used surgery, and had an extensive knowledge of the healing drugs.

Today, when physicians speak of a medical "crisis", or an "acute" infection, or a "chronic" illness they are using terms first used by Hippocrates. The oath that still guides the ethics of modern medical practitioners was probably formulated by Hippocrates.

Hippocrates declared that nothing ever happens without a natural cause. It is not surprising that he should have turned his all-encompassing attention to the phenomenon of the human fart.

In contrast to the Pythagorean ban on beans, Hippocrates taught that "passing gas is necessary to well being."[3] It is possible that he even preferred, medically speaking, a fart to a burp, for he wrote that it is "a good thing if the gathering of wind moves down to the lower regions."[4]

Hippocrates went further. He established what must surely be one of the first medically inspired noise bylaws: "It is best to emit wind without a noise ..." He then, compassionate fellow, crafted an escape clause: "But it is better to emit it even with a noise than to repress or smother it." However, he continued in the next sentence to make a most remarkable statement:

All the same, wind emitted in this manner (noisily) indicates that there is something wrong internally, or that the patient is delirious, if, at least,the emission of wind is involuntary. (EMPHASIS ADDED)

In case readers feel that they have misunderstood the good doctor, the statement is repeated in a later chapter of his work:

It is best for the passage of flatus to be silent; but it is better for its passage to be accompanied by a noise than for it not to be passed at all. However, if wind is passed noisily, it is a bad sign and indicates delirium, unless the patient deliberately emits wind thus. (EMPHASIS ADDED)

One wonders whether hapless Greek athletes who involuntarily blasted forth while hurling the discus were immediately deemed delirious and were possibly disqualified. One is also tempted to speculate that a logical corollary to the Hippocratic dictum would be that the voluntary production of a full-bodied fart was a sign of sanity. Such rarified intellectual exercise is better left to the refined minds of academics.

On balance, it is safe to say that Hippocrates certainly approved of the therapeutic value of the Vulgar Wind, but even in his day there must have been some stigma attached to it for Hippocrates to make a point of endorsement.

oOo

Rome fears death by restraint

If so, the taboo was enduring. We find it still in place in the middle of the first century AD when Tiberius Claudius Drusus Nero Germanicus (a.k.a. Claudius I) was Emperor of Rome.

Claudius may have had more than a passing acquaintance with the fart. It is a matter of record that he liked food far too well;

that he gave splendid banquets with as many as 600 guests and that he would seldom leave the table without being full to the molars and sodden with wine. It was said he slept with his mouth open and attendants would tickle his gullet with a feather so he could vomit the excess cargo. It seems likely then, that his plumbing was no stranger to excess gas.

If we are to believe his chronicler, Suetonius, Claudius was not noted for his compassion. Gladiators who accidentally stumbled and fell during arena combat had their throats cut for his edification. He would wait for hours to see victims tortured at the stake. However, there was one fate the very thought of which touched a responsive chord – the possibility of death or injury caused by restraining a common fart.

Even in licentious Rome the prohibition against the social fart was so extreme that a story went the rounds about a modest man who endangered his health by attempting self restraint. So concerned was Claudius that he contemplated "an edict to legitimize the breaking of wind at table, either silently or noisily."[5]

Apparently the edict was never officially proclaimed and we are left not knowing whether the oversight was due to the divine emperor's sodden ineptness or to the power of the anti-fart lobby.

oOo

St. Augustine praises those who sing backward

We continue, taking centuries in stride, to the early fifth century AD, to a community known by the unlikely name of Hippo (Greek for "horse") located on the Mediterranean coast of North Africa. Here, a Bishop of the Church of Rome wrote *The City of God*, a work that to this day is considered to be among the greatest of Christian theological literature. The bishop's name was Augustine, later to become St.Augustine.

Buried in the midst of *The City of God* (to be precise, in Book XIV, Chapter XXIV) there is a most amazing testimony to the eloquence of a fart, but not, one must admit, a common one. Considering the way in which the reference is made, and who makes it, we are led to suspect that the prohibition against the social fart had by this time been lightened if not lifted.

St.Augustine laments the fact that human genitals are controlled by lust rather than by will, a situation that he attributes to sin. He points out that other parts of the body are perfectly subject to the owner's will and to make his point, gives the following description:

> *There are those who can move their ears, one or both, as they please; there are those that can move all their hair towards their forehead, and back again, and never move their heads. There are those that can swallow twenty things whole, and pressing their stomach lightly, give you every thing up as whole as if they had but put into a bag. There are those that can mimic the voices of birds and other men so cunningly, that unless you see them, you cannot distinguish them at all.* There are those that can break wind backward so artificially, that you would think they sung.[6] (EMPHASIS ADDED)

It is a pity that Augustine did not give details as to who the rectal songsters were but his phrasing does not suggest that he was merely recounting hearsay. One can only assume that the research was carried out before he qualified as a saint. (Before readers scoff at St.Augustine's account let them first continue through this chapter to the 20th century and to the amazing Joseph Pujol, an entertainer at the Moulin Rouge).

oOo

Fear of the unexpelled weakens inhibitions

The Bishop of Hippo had expressed no objection to the fart. Perhaps it is this fact together with mythology accumulated over the next few centuries that helped to weaken inhibitions further. Not long after William of Normandy had conquered England we find that the physicians of the School of Salerno on the Gulf of Naples, incorporated a stern warning in their health code to the effect that unexpelled wind could cause spasms, dropsy, colic and even vertigo.*

If the school's disciples, many of whom were battle scarred crusaders, really believed that Nature administered such dire punishments for ignoring her demands for ventilation it is difficult to imagine that any social prohibitions could have had much force.

oOo

Chaucer lets fly

It is beyond the scope of this work to say whether or not the social prohibition on the Vulgar Wind may have dissipated, unlike the wind itself, throughout the following centuries. In the late 1300s in England we find a writer who stretched the sensibilities of his readers but trod with care. His name was Geoffrey Chaucer.

Chaucer understood and loved the common man but was far from being one himself. He came from a merchant family, served

—

*"Quator ex vente veniunt in ventre retente
Spamus hydrops, colica et vertigot, haec res probat ipsa."
Regimen Sanitatus Salernitatum

in a royal household, travelled widely as a diplomatic agent of the king, had possibly studied at Oxford, and could read both French and Italian. He probably wrote his most famous work, *The Canterbury Tales*, while serving as Comptroller of Customs for the Port of London.

Today, in most universities of the English speaking world, Chaucer's work is required reading for students of the humanities. An editor of one distinguished anthology has said that when it comes to English literature *The Canterbury Tales* is one of the "glories."[7]

As we track the humble fart into the bowels of English literature we find it exploding in the midst of a story narrated by a scallywag of a miller. The fact that Chaucer puts the story into the mouth of a rough member of the lower class suggests that his upper class readers might have found the content unpalatable coming from one of their own.

The miller's tale is somewhat complicated but suffice it to say that it orbits around the rivalry of two young lechers, Nicholas and Absolon, both attempting to bed the same married flirt, Alison.

Chaucer goes out of his way to give a full portrait of Absolon. After describing his hair, eyes, face and clothing he continues:

> God bless my soul, he was a merry knave!
> He knew how to let blood, cut hair and shave,
> And draw up legal deeds; at other whiles
> He used to dance in twenty different styles
> (After the current school at Oxford though,
> Casting his legs about him to and fro).
> He played a two-stringed fiddle, did it proud,
> And sang a high falsetto, rather loud;
> And he was just as good on the guitar.

There was no public house in town, or bar,
He didn't visit with his merry face
If there were saucy barmaids round the place.
He was a little squeamish in the matter
Of farting, and satirical in chatter.[8]

How are we to interpret the information that the merry Absolon, for all his accomplishments, is "a little squeamish" or, as the Middle English put it, "somdel squaymous of farting"? [9] This can be taken as proof that the anti-fart taboo endured even in Medieval England, or it may simply be taken as Chaucer's literary device planted here to make the climax of the tale more thoroughly ribald and entertaining. We leave that speculation to others and, like the miller, get on with the story.

The miller's tale reaches a complex climax (being both literary and sexual) on a memorable night when Alison's husband is decoyed out of the way and Nicholas beds her. At the same time, Absolon, not knowing of Nicholas' presence, moons outside her window calling for a kiss.

Alison, merry wench, does a little mooning on her own and lowers her bare bottom to be kissed by Absolon in the darkness. Absolon, not being quite the dunce she takes him for, goes to the local smithy, arms himself with a hot iron, returns to the window and calls for another kiss. But hold. Why condense further? Let us return to the modern translation of this astonishing example of splendid English literature.

Now Nicholas had risen for a piss,
And thought he could improve upon the jape
And make him kiss his arse ere he escape,
And opening the window with a jerk,
Stuck out his arse, a handsome piece of work,

Buttocks and all, as far as to the haunch.
Said Absolon, all set to make a launch,
"Speak, pretty bird, I know not where thou art!"
This Nicholas at once let fly a fart
As loud as if it were a thunder-clap.
He was near blinded by the blast, poor chap,
But his hot iron was ready; with a thump
He smote him in the middle of the rump.[10]

It was well for Absolon that Nicholas was not of the Blue Angel family or his ploy might have backfired and sent a blue flame shimmering down through the annals of English literature along with the thunder-clap.

With the fart blessed, or at the very least well entrenched by both St.Augustine and Geoffrey Chaucer, let us see where else our pursuit of the wily wind takes us.

oOo

Rabelais' life-unifying air

We come now to France in the first half of the 1500s and find a satirist and humourist, François Rabelais, farting and belching through his pen with such abandon that the adjective "Rabelaisian" has entered our own language to describe indelicate humour. Indeed, a fart was a mere bagatelle to Rabelais. In one yarn he listed more than sixty substitutes for toilet paper, finally recommending the downy neck of a live goose.[11]

Rabelais can be tough going for the modern layperson, although our scholars like to find deep spiritual values in his grotesqueries. Indeed, the Rabelaisian Fart has been said to have spiritual value because it is connected with the air that unifies all of life. (Could this be why children laugh with such delight at an elder's impromptu explosion? Do they intuitively recognize a commonality with their elders, and greet the revelation with joy?)

oOo

Montaigne laments life-threatening release

Wafting onward into the later 1500s in France we find the writings of Michel Eyquem de Montaigne, considered to be one of the great essayists of Europe, who wrote on a wide variety of subjects.

One famous essay was *On the Power of Imagination.* Here we find him not only mentioning St. Augustine's remarkable reference but also saying that the bishop's commentator, Vives, went the saint one better and described "farts arranged to suit the tone of verses pronounced to their accompaniment."

Montaigne is not about to be outdone by Vives. He adds, "I know one (a behind) so turbulent and unruly, that for forty years it has kept its master farting with a constant and unremitting wind and compulsion, and is thus taking him to his death."[12]

This is a curious comment. It was more usual for the retention of flatus to be considered dangerous but Montaigne seems to have thought the constant release could be life-threatening. Perhaps he was thinking the "unremitting wind" might bring retaliation from sword-wielding peers. However, in the 1595 edition of his work he subscribes to the orthodox view and laments,

Would God I knew only from the history books how many times our stomach, by refusing *one single fart, brings us to the gates of a very anguished death.*[13] (EMPHASIS ADDED)

We shall examine this "anguished death" statement in a more clinical chapter. Suffice it to say at the moment that unless the Renaissance fart was more virile than its modern descendants, Montaigne administered our humble subject a bum rap (not to be confused with the rap administered by Chaucer's Absolon).

About the same time Montaigne was eulogizing the power of imagination (only an essayist could take a subject so far astray) the Earl of Oxford was paying his noisy homage to the throne of England, referred to in our introductory chapter. As noted there, although the act apparently was not considered proper court etiquette the word itself was certainly Queen's English since it was used publicly by the Queen herself. However, action speaking louder than words, Oxford did go into exile. The taboo that Chaucer had infringed with such gusto was still firmly seated in Elizabethan England.

oOo

Swift explains the blast that puts out fires

By the early 18th century we find Irish born Jonathan Swift savagely writing a niche for himself as one of the greatest of English satirists. Not only did he write the cutting political allegory, *Gulliver's Travels,* (passed off these days as a tale for children) but also wittily abrasive treatises on politics, conversation, poetry and manners. In a gently corrosive attack upon the overly elaborate and stultifying manners of the upper classes he said,

...all the civilized nations of the world have agreed upon fixing some rules for common behaviour... as a kind of artificial good sense, to supply the defects of reason.[14]

Swift did not say whether or not the prohibition against the humble fart was an example of "artificial good sense" rather than of reason, but a remarkable publication came off a London press in the year 1727. Although it appeared under a pseudonym, some scholars attributed it to the punning pen of Jonathan Swift.

It is only fair to remind the reader that Swift, that learned Dean of St.Patrick's in Dublin, has quite a sufficiency of other unusual credits where authorship is not in question. Indeed, part of his penetrating view of the human animal has been called "the excremental vision,"[15] a term that indicates he went far beyond mere allusions to the airy fart. The mischievous wind was well within Swift's literary embrace.

In a poem, *Strephon and Chloe,* he gave interesting advice on the rearing of daughters:

> Keep them to wholsome Food confin'd,
> Nor let them taste what causes Wind;*
> ('Tis this the sage of Samos means,
> Forbidding his Disciples Beans)
> O, think what Evils must ensue;
> Miss Moll the Jade will burn it blue;
> And when she once has got the Art,
> She cannot help it for her Heart;
> But, out it flies, even when she meets
> Her Bridegroom in the Wedding-Sheets.
> Carminative and Diuretick,
> Will damp all Passion Sympathetick;
> And, Love such Nicety requires,
> One Blast will put out all his fires.[16] *

---

*These two lines contain a truly explosive paradox that will come to light in Chapter Five.

So one is not straying far afield to attribute the publication of 1727 to Swift. The title page is said to be "the finest title-page of the eighteenth century".[17] Once that page disposes of the title itself, *The Benefit of Farting Explained*, it is chock-a-block full of puns.

The piece pretends to have been written by a Spaniard, Don Fartinhando Puffindorst, Professor of Bumbast at the University of Craccow, and to have been translated for the use of Lady Dampfart, of Herfartshire. It claims to prove "*a posteriori*" that most of the disorders "in-tail'd on" the fair sex are owing to "flatulencies not seasonably vented." (Even here we see a repetition of the old fear of suppressing rectal ventilation.) For modern eyes the puns are less than subtle but the original printer made copious use of hyphens and italics to make certain the reader did not miss any of them.

This astonishing title page even includes two verses that may (or may not) have originated with Jonathan Swift. They read easily when printed in modern typeface without any need to update the spelling:

> A Fart, tho' wholesome does not fail,
> If barred of passage by the tail,
> To fly back to the head again,
> And by its fumes disturb the brain.
>
> Thus gunpowder confin'd, you know Sir,
> Grows stronger, as 'tis ram'd the closer;
> But, if in open air it fires,
> In harmless smoke its force expires.[18]

One cannot help but note that the author considers flatulence to be a female "distemper." Superficially this appears to be an amazing conclusion when we know the human animal produces waste gases without fear, favour, affection, or sexual preference. The assumption may be more of a comment on the absurdly restrictive feminine clothing of the day than on any organic lack of propriety amongst women.

It may also imply that men, usually more vulgar anyway, were more apt to let the wind blow freely. Among the men, being horsemen all, a saying still heard in the 20th century may have been prevalent:

> A farting horse will never tire –
> [therefore] A farting man's the man to hire.

oOo

Balzac's ambition for a most natural thing

One is tempted to remain in England and break a little wind with the famous poet and artist William Blake, but instead let us canter onwards into the mid 19th century and proceed again to France. Here we find the superb French writer, Honoré de Balzac, being quoted as having a most unusual ambition.

"I should like one of these days," he is reported to have said, "to be so well known, so popular, so celebrated, so famous, that it would permit me to break wind in society and society would think it a most natural thing."[19]

Apparently, in spite of such yearnings and in spite of all evidence to the contrary, it was still not considered a "natural thing," even in France.

The literati, however, were no more easily subdued than is our wayward subject. We, and it, waft onward to Hartford, Connecticut, USA, and to the year 1882. Here, Samuel Clemens, already widely acclaimed under the pen name Mark Twain as the author of *The Adventures of Tom Sawyer*, wrote a private piece of satire for the enjoyment of his close friend, the Reverend Joseph Twichell.

A few years previously Twain and Twichell had journeyed together on a walking trip through the Black Forest and Switzerland. One can only assume that while sharing the rough meals of the wayside they became increasingly aware that man's time-seasoned friend the fart was constantly with them. At any rate, a few years later a treatise on the same common fellow emerged from the tip of Twain's pen.

The full title of the little opus was *Mark Twain's [Date, 1601] Conversation As it was by the Social Fireside in the Time of the Tudors.*[20] Today it is often spoken of simply as *1601*. The "conversation" in said tale allegedly took place at an Elizabethan soiree where the principal participants were Queen Elizabeth I, Sir Walter Raleigh, Sir Francis Bacon, Ben Jonson, Francis Beaumont and, of course, Shakespeare. In addition to the Queen, there were several court ladies present.

"In ye heat of ye talk it befell yt one did breake wind," wrote Twain. He portrayed the Queen as being mightily impressed: "Verily in mine eight and sixty yeres I have not heard ye fellow to this fart. Meseemeth, by ye grete sound and clamour of it, it was male."

All eyes turn on the men and one after the other, in fulsome rounded phrases parodying Elizabethan high flown dramatic literature, they protest their innocence. The adjectives accumulate in rhetorical splendour:

... a thundergust ... this rich o'ermastering fog, this fragrant gloom ... matchless might ... a hurricane ... so fell a blast ... this prodigy ... this miracle ... this most desolating breath ... Heaven's artillery.

It is Sir Walter Raleigh who finally pleads guilty and apologizes, as befits a good Elizabethan, for mediocrity.

... 'twas I that did it, but indeed it was so poor and frail a note, compared with such as I am wont to furnish, yt in sooth I was ashamed to call the weakling mine in so august a presence. It was nothing – less than nothing, madam – I did it but to clear my nether throat; but had I come prepared, then had I delivered something worthy. Bear with me, please your grace, till I can make amends.

The dauntless Raleigh then "delivered himself of such a godless and rock-shivering blast that all were fain to stop their ears."[21]

1601 was published clandestinely at West Point Military Academy, a fact that must tell us something about the paradoxical position of the fart in 19th century America. Its position is still up in the air.

In 1963 two American scholars published *A Mark Twain Lexicon.*[22] An introduction claimed that "A total of nearly eight thousand words, combinations, and meanings have been selected from the vocabulary of Mark Twain's published writings for inclusion in this Lexicon." A footnote explains further that "An original total of over ten thousand words was reduced by extensive elimination."

Unfortunately, in 266 pages of typeface that would give a hawk eyestrain, the humble fart, "this prodigy, this miracle," was eliminated. The two scholars compounded the paradox by including a quote from Walt Whitman's *An American Primer*:

The Real Dictionary will give all words that exist in use, the bad words as well as any ... Do you suppose the liberties and brawn of These States have to do only with delicate lady-words? with gloved gentleman words?[23]

oOo

Le Petomane's astonishing 'singing' repertoire

But we get ahead of ourselves. One short decade after Twain's literary explosion was saved for posterity by the American military establishment, members of high society in France were patronizing a remarkable performer who dominated the stage of the Moulin Rouge. Here, in 1892, an act began that entranced audiences for the next three years.

The artist was Joseph Pujol. He performed under the stage name of Le Petomane, which can be translated, keeping a whiff of the French atmosphere, as The Farteur. Years later, Pujol's son recalled that his father's rectal repertoire was accompanied by verbal patter making comparisons with such varied endeavours as a mason working with mortar that was too dry , a cannon being fired, and a dressmaker tearing two metres of calico. Apparently it took ten seconds for the calico tear.[24]

Pujol's repertoire also included imitations of a yapping pup, a dog with its tail caught in a door, a mocking blackbird, a laughing owl, a crowing cock, a singing duck, a humming bee, a laying hen, a copulating tomcat, and even a nightingale.

A contemporary described the Moulin Rouge audience as laughing, crying, and even screaming with delight at Le

Petomane's "incongruities." He also described streaming eyes, faces apoplectically contorted with laughter, and tightly corseted women being helped away by nurses until they could retrieve their breath.

The reader may consider this to be a strange form of theatrical entertainment but at the height of his career Pujol apparently earned more than did the "divine" Sarah Bernhardt, the doyenne of actresses.

Le Petomane performed at the Moulin Rouge until 1894 and then, after an altercation with management, established a family theatre and even took his act on tour. He received poor reviews from the nonplussed Spaniards but his artistic career continued until the outbreak of war in 1914. He died in 1945.

Joseph Pujol was not, alas, a true exponent of the common fart. He did not rely on self manufactured gases. His secret lay in having absolute control of the anal sphincter and of his abdominal muscles. He could ingest air through this sphincter and then expel it again under such force and control as to create the remarkable sounds already described. Using his abdominal muscles as a bellows, he could blow out a candle flame from the distance of a foot. He could also imbibe water in this novel way, and expel it a distance of five yards.[25]

Pujol's accomplishments, if not those of a farteur of natural gas, at least give support to the claims of St. Augustine and also serve to remind us that society's current proscription on the Vulgar Wind is not only fragile but quite possibly hypocritical. Pujol's biographers claim that he even 'sang' for King Leopold II of Belgium.

oOo

Ecclesiastical, dinner and stage punctuations

The wind continues to blow where it listeth through 20th century literature. A character in J.D. Salinger's famous novel, *Catcher in the Rye*, describes a "terrific fart" in church, and allows that in spite of its crudity it was entertaining.

The fart-in-church has always been a pointed source of merriment, creating internal forces of suppressed laughter that seem to threaten life more surely than ever did frustrated flatus. This ecclesiastical prohibition is puzzling when one considers that Nature and God are, if not one and the same, at least in league with one another.

The fart in less rarified surroundings is common in modern literature. It even finds a place in biography. Peter Townsend, who was affiliated professionally with Britain's royal household and romantically with Princess Margaret, describes a dowager duchess who unconcernedly punctuated her dinner table conversation with flatulent colons. He draws a pleasantly charming picture of astonished guests who "either looked fixedly at the ceiling and bit their lips, or conversed, shouting at each other, hoping to drown the cannonade."[26]

It must have been a similar duchess who inspired a limerick:

I sat next to the Duchess at tea;
It was just as I feared it would be:
Her rumblings abdominal
Were simply phenomenal,
And everyone thought it was me![27]

The greatly loved British actor, Sir John Mills, recalls in his gentle memoirs a performance of a 1936 play suitably titled,

Aren't Men Beasts? It took place at the Strand Theatre and starred Mills, Robertson "Bunny" Hare and Alfred Drayton.

"On one momentous occasion," recalls Mills, "at a matinee, after I can only suppose a large helping of baked beans for lunch ... Bunny jumped as usual into the air and a foot from the stage produced one of the loudest and most spectacular farts it has ever been my pleasure to hear. There was no question this time of it being an 'in' joke – the audience heard it. There was no need to go through the agony of suppressing the laughter; the house went up in smoke and we went up with it."[28]

oOo

A Canadian lover's agonizing deflation

Canadian author, Donald Jack, creator of the indomitable Bartholomew Bandy and three times winner of Canada's prestigious Stephen Leacock Medal for humour, describes his hero caught, as it were, *in flatus delicto* while in bed with his paramour, Anne. We quote a rather lengthy excerpt (permission having been granted by Mr. Jack whose generosity outruns his good sense) because it is surely one of the most detailed descriptions of a single fart ever to grace the pages of modern literature:

I waited, with sinking heart, stomach, lights, liver, etc., lying there with wide-open eyes and tightly closed sphincter, hoping that the pressure would die down of its own accord, or at least reverse itself and pulse back all the way to my duodenum. But the pressure gradually increased, as if the bacilli had decided to go for broke.

It must have been that fresh-baked bread that George had brought back from the boulangerie. And I couldn't release the air because the nasal hubbub had already brought Anne close to the surface of consciousness. She was now almost as restless as I was. If I let go, the sound would almost certainly issue forth as a veritable trumpet voluntary. The bedclothes would probably billow as well, assuming they weren't blasted off entirely with a rending of sheets and a cloud of feathers. Anne would be absolutely disgusted – or worse, asphyxiated, for I knew how noxious dough- created fumes could be. I tried to think beautiful thoughts, hoping to tap the tranquil mind's ability to subdue its own functions, but I had reckoned without the intestinal fortitude. It was either let go or confirm Robbie Burns's Let wind gae free where'er you be, for 'tis wind that was the death of me.

There was only one thing for it. Carefully reaching over Anne's sleeping form, I covered her face with the sheet; then, inch by inch, hauled out the bedclothes on my side, cursing myself for having tucked them so firmly under the mattress; then slowly maneuvered until my bare behind was exposed to the chill air; and with bated breath, so to speak, concentrated on loosing the appropriate valve a quarter turn at a time, releasing the pressure as slowly and discreetly as possible, in a long, tightly controlled flow.

The faint hissing went on for so long that I began to get worried, imagining my entire form slowly deflating like the world's largest sausage balloon. I had a frightful picture of Anne waking up in the morning to find nothing left of me but a puckered end – assuming she was not found dead in bed from fresh bread.

But the emission finally ended, concluding its efforts with a stertorous burst and a faint bubbling. ...I remembered the brand-new Russian proverb that had been going the rounds while I was in Moscow, to wit, If there were no birds, a commissar's fart would sound like a nightingale.[29]

Modern poetry is no more sheltered from the wind than is modern prose. Without even leaving decorously conservative Canada one finds poet Irving Layton dedicating a verse to a farting priest: "To the Priest Who Kept My Wife Awake All Night, Farting."[30]

oOo

Beans assault the screen

When sampling the atmosphere of the arts one cannot ignore film and television. They surround us almost as completely as does the ubiquitous wind.

In 1974, the irrepressible Mel Brooks and his cohorts rode out of Hollywood on *Blazing Saddles*, a film that did for cowboys what Monty Python's *Holy Grail* did for King Arthur's knights. *Blazing Saddles* delivers a series of comic jolts, none of which is more startling than the sudden flooring of a horse by means of a right uppercut, but a most unusual scene occurs around a campfire after the cowboys have had the traditional meal of good baked beans. Before the moviegoers' startled eyes and ears, they enter into a shooting contest complete with cocked legs and sound effects. The audience is relieved when the sequence ends with no one having fired anything more obnoxious than blanks.

The bean sequence was deleted from the version distributed for television broadcast, which raises the question of whether the fart is deemed to be acceptable in public gatherings but not in the privacy of one's home.

Since that time the Vulgar Wind has managed to waft across the screen, both silver and cathode, at more and more frequent intervals. In a screen version of James Heriott's delightful *All Creatures Great and Small*, a silently-flatulent dog threads its way quietly and unseen amongst the guests at a cocktail party leaving a trail of confusion behind as the guests eye each other warily and attempt to distance themselves each from each other.

By late 1992 the fart made its way into the popular television series, *L.A.Law*, when a senior partner of the highly respectable law firm found himself imprisoned in a cell with a flatulent convict whose rectal monosyllables were stated with clarity and fanned with desperation.

A scene that was handled with more refinement and more symbolism took place in a 1986 feature film called *Labyrinth*. This is a film by the late Jim Henson of Muppet fame. It mixes delightful Muppet-inspired creatures with live actors (including David Bowie) in a children's adventure story of considerable charm and inventiveness. At one point the heroine and her cohorts have to cross the "bog of eternal stench." So complete is the bog with visual bubblings and burbling eruptions and reprehensible sound effects that no child of any age could possibly mistake the identity of the bog. It is as though Creation itself had turned bottom up. Such scenes epitomize the Vulgar Wind for lo, the latter is with us always, in the midst of art as in the midst of life, and while we seem compelled to shun it and attempt to pass over it, it is always beneath us and we can never ignore it.

oOo

Assimilating the wind

Since we cannot ignore the Wind, we may as well civilize it, or at least assimilate it. The best place to start is with language.

CHAPTER
FOUR

The Wind and the Words

Creativity from The Merck Manual
Not so distant drums
Sawing the ping-pong table
Shunning vulgarity
CBC creates and the US Navy circulates
Lengthening the lexicon
Civilizing the mud-duck
Acronyms for accuracy
Life without humiliation

CHAPTER
FOUR

The Wind and the Words

The observant reader will have noticed by now that in spite of St. Augustine's songsters, Chaucer's thunderclap, the Earl of Oxford's disgrace, Swift's professor of bumbast, and even Twain's prodigious miracle, we have come across no new words to replace the humble fart. There are adjectives enough to form a minor lexicon but fresh nouns and verbs remain sadly lacking. This is a disgrace for a language that is said to contain 600,000 words (a considerable increase from the mere 140,000 that were around for Shakespeare to play with).[1]

One would think that with the addition of well over 1000 new words per year, English-speaking tongues might have created a few handy alternatives to "fart." This scarcity of flatulent synonyms can only be attributed to the influence of those in society who, feeling themselves to have risen above Nature , dictate the way in which lesser mortals speak of what is natural.

It is time we joined in the fight to break the linguistic bonds and to enrich the aroma of the language. Thankfully, we are not alone. It is a struggle where others have pioneered before us.

oOo

Creativity from The Merck Manual

In doctors' offices throughout North America one finds a rather large reference work called *The Merck Manual.*[2] It is a handy and some say indispensable guide for doctors wishing to check on symptoms and signs leading to diagnosis. In the section on intestinal gas The Manual indulges in creative classification: (Please note that the following bracketed interjections are part of this quote)

This symptom, which can cause great psychosocial distress, has been unofficially and humorously described according to its salient characteristics:
(1) the 'slider' (crowded elevator type), which is released slowly and noiselessly, sometimes with devastating effect;
(2) the open sphincter, or 'pooh' type, which is said to be of higher temperature and more aromatic;
(3) the staccato or drum-beat type, pleasantly passed in privacy;
(4) the 'bark' type (described in a personal communication) is characterized by a sharp exclamatory eruption that effectively interrupts (and often concludes) conversation. Aromaticity is not a prominent feature.

With admiring acknowledgement to *The Merck Manual* we appropriate the term "slider." One can drop a slider, lay a slider, slip a slider or even, presumably, slide, for example: "Someone in the assembly, working incognito, slid a temporary pall over the conversation."

It must surely have been a colossal slider that disturbed the sleep of Bartholomew Bandy. We endorse the word if not the action.

It is tempting to appropriate the term "bark," but the word is so well entrenched at the other anatomical extremity that it might cause dangerous confusion, as in "barking dogs never bite."

oOo

Not so distant drums

Taking inspiration from *The Merck Manual's* "drumbeat type," let us turn our attention to the art of the drummer. This is a fertile field for useful terminology. With a little imagination we can adapt the names of percussive strokes to the requirements of explosive wind. The "paradiddle," the "flam," the "drag," the "ruff" are all good candidates, being suitable as verbs, nouns, or even interjections. For example: "It was embarrassing. Flam! Right in the middle of an embrace. No one else there. Just her and me and the phone booth."

Or, to paraphrase a line from *My Fair Lady:* "Oozing gas from every pore, he ruffed his way across the floor."

Judicious use of such terms can add a whole new dimension to the subtleties of life and literature: "Hey paradiddle, the cat and the fiddle ..." At last we know how the cow jumped over the moon.

It is not being suggested that such words be used only when the farteur has managed to emulate the intricate art of the drummer but rather that the drummer's vocabulary can be adapted.[3] Emulating a drum roll composed of recurring double beats would challenge the most sophisticated sphincter, but its name of "Mammy-Daddy" can be renovated to designate considerable status. It would work best as a single word, a veritable mommadaddy of a word. Then even the most proper historian could write: "The Earl laid such a mommadaddy before the throne that he blew himself into exile."

oOo

Sawing the ping-pong table

There are at least three novelty booklets on the market that purport to catalogue the Vulgar Wind. They list well over 100 categories, many of which are best left in limbo, and most of which are not stand-alone labels so much as descriptive adjectives having more to do with the circumstances of delivery than with the quality of production.

In one of those quirky volumes, however, there is one label, the "skillsaw," that has a certain aptness.[4] It is described as the sound made "sawing the ping-pong table in half" and is undoubtedly a close relative of the "calico" or "dressmaker" as performed by Joseph Pujol. These would come under *The Merck Manual* category of "the staccato or drum-beat type."

We recommend keeping "skillsaw" in reserve for monumental staccato achievements and using "calico" for more modest occasions. Calico is an inoffensive word that lends itself to homespun gentility: "Miss Mayfair, stooping to retrieve her fan, produced a pleasing calico." It can even be a verb: "As the dance ended, Miss Mayfair calicoed a curtsy."

oOo

Shunning vulgarity

Following advice from a younger generation, the author turned with some anticipation to recordings of the night club routines of American comedians.

True enough, they had not overlooked the Vulgar Wind.

Alas, they had not omitted any bodily function, and had done it in the modern style that confuses shock with wit and vulgarity for humour. It was necessary to look elsewhere for inspiration.

oOo

CBC creates and the US Navy circulates

The definitive work in categorization comes from Canada, a virile country said to get so cold in winter that flatus freezes until reactivated by the spring thaw at which time it creates a sound like distant cannon that the citizens pretend is caused by the breakup of the ice in their northern lakes.

In the late 1940s Canada, or more precisely, the Canadian Broadcasting Corporation (CBC), was the home of what was widely recognized as the best radio drama in the English speaking world. Sometime during that period an unauthorized production slid from within the CBC studios.

This clandestine record then drifted privately through the sound suites of radio stations, film studios and other centres of Canadian grassroots culture. It was called, *The Crepitation Contest.*

The record bore no label giving artists' credits but the writer and principal performer was widely rumoured to be a member of the CBC staff, as was the sound effects man. Reliable information also tells us that a supporting actor was a senior executive with the Canadian branch of a famous record company. The program was produced, presumably on a quiet weekend, in Studio G of CBC Toronto's old Jarvis Street studios.

Rumours further suggest that more than a thousand pressings were made – during off-hours of course – using the facilities of the record company. It is also said that the major world-wide distributor was the US Navy with pressings appearing as far away as

Japan. Thus *The Crepitation Contest* is a worthy companion to Mark Twain's *1601* having been saved for posterity not, in this case, by the US Army but by the US Navy. This seems to add credibility of a sort, to the far-reaching influence of the American military above and beyond the call of duty.

Complete with imperturbable announcer and impeccable sound effects, the recording pretends to bring the listener on-the-spot coverage of a contest and does to sports broadcasting what Twain did to Elizabethan dramatic literature. As with any sophisticated sport, there are traditions, statistics, rules and several levels of achievement. In describing all this to the audience the creators of this vulgar masterpiece coined or appropriated several useful terms.[5]

oOo

Lengthening the lexicon

First, the title itself. "Crepitation" is not, strictly speaking, an exact synonym for flatus because it is also used medically to describe the sound of broken bone ends rubbing together. It does indicate, however, a crackling sound. Consequently it performs as a reasonable noun and adjective. It has an advantage over many other words in that it already has a verb. "To crepitate" is already in the language whereas "to calico" is not. We recommend the verb "to crepitate" as long as it is used to indicate the production of a calico, a dressmaker, or even of a skillsaw.

"Crepitation," however, does not cover the heavy punctuation that can be achieved by a drum's subdued roll followed by a heavy beat. *The Crepitation Contest's* name for the parallel flatological phenomenon was "flutterblast." It could escalate to a "triple flutterblast." "Flutterblast" is a good noun but not a great verb.

The intrepid CBC artists came up with the term, "freep." This is a good word, being short and sharp, making an excellent verb and requiring no further explanation.

In searching for a description more believable than Twain's "heaven's artillery" the disciples of the Jarvis Street muse created "fundusbreak," an amazing word with suitable depth and power. As a word it is not as pliable as freep but it has some use as a noun. Fundusbreak does not make an elegant verb although it works in the past tense: "The three-to-one favourite fundusbroke in the gate and the whole field, thinking the gun had gone, took off."

As a noun, fundusbreak can be escalated by suitable adjectives: "The groom paused in front of the mansion door. He swept the bride into his arms and, as he did so, laid a mommadaddy fundusbreak upon the threshold. As the echoes rang from the lintel it dawned upon the bride that her Galahad, her Prince Charming, was as human as any other man. It was a revelation that would spare her much disillusionment in the years to come."

Another word coined for the Contest was "plotcher." As may be surmised, a plotcher was an infringement of the rules and so does not belong in our list of useful synonyms although it could have a literary use: "A look of consternation spread over her face as she realized a plotcher had just soiled her fragile aura of sweet sophistication."

Thus to slider, calico, dressmaker, skillsaw, paradiddle, flam, drag, ruff and mommadaddy, we can add to our lexicon the involuntary contribution of the austere Canadian Broadcasting Corporation: crepitate (noun, adjective and verb); flutterblast (noun); freep (noun and verb); fundusbreak (noun and verb).

oOo

Civilizing the mud-duck

There is another word currently in use among film crews. It is "mud-duck," so named after the sound a large duck would make pulling its foot out of mud. This is a versatile noun that also makes a vigorous verb: "Standing there in the middle of the room, a martini in his hand and a bon mot on his lips, the poor guy mud-ducked."

It is also a term that if adopted more widely could easily be shortened, becoming almost genteel: "As a gesture of defiance and frustration he ducked and left the room." Readers of a delicate turn of mind are permitted to assume there was a low doorway.

oOo

Acronyms for accuracy

In addition to our now expanded vocabulary, there circulates another entire system of nomenclature that is of unknown origin. It makes use of acronyms, has no verbs and while the system is slightly cumbersome, it is extremely accurate. Since it is self-explanatory we will simply present a list. There are other variations but we recommend the following because the acronyms are all pronounceable:

SAD (Silent And Deadly)
SAND (Silent And Not Deadly)
NAND (Noisy And Not Deadly)
NAD (Noisy and Deadly)

The SAND is the most innocuous, being known only to its creator. SADs and NADs are dangerous fellows: "He dropped a NAD that not only shook the room but shortly thereafter emptied it." The NAND is the hale fart well met.

oOo

Life without humiliation

It is obvious even from these few suggestions that the language is capable of much more colour and accuracy than St. Augustines' cumbersome, "break wind backwards." But it is equally obvious that a fart, no matter how dressed, is still a fart.

There is something untameable about both the word and the action. It seems pointless for society to persist in attempts at boycott.

Therefore, now that we have posed the problems facing the Vulgar Wind (Chapter One), explained its mechanics (Chapter Two), reviewed its history (Chapter Three) and expanded its vocabulary (Chapter Four), let us examine ways to cope with the troublesome fellow so that we may all live without dissonance, discord, or undue humiliation.

CHAPTER
FIVE

Going With the Wind

In tranquility if not in silence
Abberation, suppression, obliteration?
Fossilized dinofarteurs
Blue Angels as elite power brokers
A word of warning
Coping with the occasional wayward transgression
Denial, the simplest device
Genteel dialogue and ungenteel attribution
Purgatives: Sulphur, salts and 'perpetual pills'
Perils of inadvertant air gulping
A healthy diet is a breezy diet
The inflationary FF Index
Tampering with natural phenomena
Studies in long term deflation
A strange source of flatulence

CHAPTER
FIVE

Going With the Wind

By now, it has surely become abundantly clear that the common fart is an integral part of the human condition. Unless human beings evolve into biological machines that burn a waste-free fuel (the only one that comes to mind is electricity, and even it has to be generated) then the fart is surely with us always, even unto the very end of time.

oOo

In tranquility if not in silence

The hour has come when we must stop denying the fart by pretending to ignore it. We must, at long last, learn to live with it in tranquility, if not in silence. Banishing ourselves from society, as did the Earl of Oxford, is no longer an acceptable solution. Indeed, it never was a remedy – a truth known to the limerist:

"I'm off!" cried a sinner who sinned
By noisily breaking some wind,
"With my airs and my wiles
I abandon these isles!"—
But 'twasn't the last din he dinned.

oOo

Abberation, suppression, obliteration?

There will always be some in society who will refuse to compromise; who may even become militant, and not only denounce the fart as an aberration, but actively campaign to have it suppressed, even obliterated. Such extremism may be fueled by a humble work such as this. Indeed, statistics carried herein are subject to disturbing interpretations.

It has been estimated that the daily personal passing of gas can *average* as high as 2400 ml.[1] Each emission can be composed of any one or all of the five major gases, along with contaminating volatiles such as hydrogen sulphide. If one multiplies the daily individual emission by the number of human beings in the world, then the total quantity of gas released every day is not only remarkable but is increasing at the same alarming rate as is the world population.

It is not too great a stretch of the imagination to picture the more rabid environmentalists claiming that mankind is damaging the atmosphere through flatulence alone.

Some time ago the author was intrigued to hear a guest on CBC Radio's national network science program, *Quirks and Quarks*, claim that methane from animal flatulence is contributing to global warming and other problems. He laid much of the blame on cattle, claiming they account for about three quarters of animal methane emissions. Apparently up to 9% of a cow's intake goes out in gas.[2] Today, as every newspaper reader knows, it is commonplace to hear of studies investigating the effect of animal methane on the greenhouse effect.

oOo

Fossilized dinofarteurs

It is only fair to report that scientists who have been nosing around the fossilized dung of dinosaurs recently conjectured that dinosaur flatulence some 80 million years ago may have released enough methane to have contributed to global warming during the Cretaceous period.[3] Quite apart from the gaseous concern, one is forced to ponder the acoustical implications of a herd of dinofarteurs. Surely such gargantuan and terrifying thunder must have triggered earthquakes, rock slides and other disasters. And no wonder the beasts were designed with nose so far from tail.

The measuring of animal flatulence is becoming an environmental sub-specialty as organizations like The Worldwatch Institute, The Environmental Protection Agency, Environment Canada, and a host of others are busily estimating animal gas production. Current figures are in the neighbourhood of 100 million tonnes annually. It is not clear to this writer whether, as members of the animal kingdom, we are taking our own production into account. One hopes so. After all, as poet Alexander Pope noted in his *An Essay on Man*, "The proper study of mankind is Man."

Conceivably, the fact that each of us – men, women and children – contributes to air pollution could be used to create a powerful, indeed pervasive argument against overpopulation. It would be Orwellian indeed to find society using abortion, euthanasia and mandatory birth control as principal tools to suppress the fart.

oOo

Blue Angels as elite power brokers

People of a more conservative, traditional turn of mind, dedicated to economic growth and the full utilization of resources,may someday see a quite different challenge. In the future when fossil fuels have become depleted or banned, entrepreneurs may harness the energy potential of that happy segment of the population producing their own personal combustible methane.

The ability is already known to be a familial trait and it may well be that some such families are even more gifted than others. The day may come when those who are blessed by the Blue Angels may form an upper class elite that will give new meaning to the political term "power brokers."

oOo

A word of warning

Such scenarios are of little immediate practical use. They are more suited to exercising the imagination than to coping with an imminent, or eminent fart. But a word of warning is warranted.

There is already a case on record of a university student in Florida being ticketed by police for releasing the wild wind. The suspect was subsequently reported as saying that he meant no disrespect and had no idea that the decibel level was so high. Be that as it may, the charge was laid under an obnoxious odour bylaw. However, the judge may have also been a person of unusual intestinal fortitude because the charge was dismissed.[4]

oOo

Coping with the occasional wayward transgression

Coping with the fart can be a challenge to our skills, especially our verbal ones. Honesty can be an effective tool, tempered with humour, compassion, and diplomacy. Useful, too, are the arts of the doctor, psychologist and dietitian. We will discuss their remedies in a moment but first let us consider ways to handle the occasional wayward fart whose presence is perceived as a simple social transgression.

It is a rare person who doesn't occasionally emit anything from a calico to a fundusbreak at an inopportune time. The most awkward moment is the one where the perpetrator, under the impression he is alone, permits a full bodied and unmuffled release, sometimes even going so far as to cock a leg to give full egress to the vagrant airs, only to turn around and find a colleague, or the Queen, or the boss's wife, transfixed in the doorway.

There is no remedy for such a trespass on decorum other than instant and mutual amnesia, self immolation, or Oxford's voluntary exile. If one elects, wilfully and grossly, to violate social niceties then one must pay the price of social disapproval.

oOo

Denial , the simplest device

In order to maintain some vestige of propriety there are other devices we can use. The most obvious is simple denial.

Our concern here is for the emission that comes involuntarily and is virtually uncontrollable. If it is a mere freep it can safely be ignored, the course of action recommended by Miss Manners, the whimsical arbiter of social good taste. Under the heading of "Unacceptable Noises" she says:

Miss Manners does not plan to mention them, chiefly because they are unmentionable, but you all know who you are. What they are. At any rate, these are noises that are acknowledged by neither the noisemaker nor the noise recipient, because socially they do not exist.[5]

This advice is fine as long as it merely applies to the simple freep, but denial of existence is unacceptable as the scale increases. Putting one's head in the sand is no way to suppress flatus. The fart, being a forceful individual and at the same time part of a universal collectivity, will not be denied. It insists on the right to a hearing.

An interesting form of denial is found, poorly explained, in the pages of 19th century literature where one meets ladies who faint under an attack of "the vapours." The vapours were exhalations of the stomach thought to induce hysteria. Fainting, feigned or hysterical, was possibly an attempt to deny flatulent reality. Today, neither culture nor corsets demand such extreme deception.

Some people use the subterfuge of a discreet cough to deny a freep by suggesting it is merely a tentative clearing of the throat. This is not only unnecessary but dangerous.

A cough is often more germ laden than any fart and so one is covering indiscretion with thoughtlessness. Inconsideration is compounded by recklessness because the cough itself can cause a convulsion that jars the sensitive sphincter, often releasing a NAND or even a NAD.* This adverse result encourages the

—

*NAND meaning Noisy and Not Deadly. NAD meaning Noisy and Deadly.

farteur into the folly of diverting attention with an even stronger cough, thus escalating the problem into fundusbreaking dimensions.

The conclusion is obvious. The freep is an inconsequential fellow. If one escapes, so be it. One can even follow the lead of Twain's Sir Walter Raleigh and deny it on the grounds of mediocrity. This of course does not apply to more complex presentations, such as sliders.

Some unscrupulous producers of cocktail party sliders have developed the knack of casting a slight glance of disapproval at an innocent neighbour and almost imperceptibly veering away as though wishing to be separated from the source without giving undue offence. This diversion of attention is a denial of responsibility. It is not easy to condone such dishonesty. Miss Manners agrees:

The practice of staring hard at the person next to you when, for instance, your own stomach has given off a loud rumble, is therefore to be condemned on grounds of etiquette as well as morals.[6]

If diverting responsibility for a mere abdominal "rumble" can violate morality, what a sin it must be to divert responsibility for a skillsaw, flutterblast, or slider.

Denial then, in the sense of simply ignoring some feeble flatus, is quite acceptable, but to acknowledge the presence of a major effort while denying parenthood, is not acceptable.

The more clamorous productions defy denial, and present a social challenge to the creators and to their companions; a challenge that can be met, as is only fitting, vocally.

oOo

Genteel dialogue and ungenteel attribution

Ignoring the NAND, as did the dowager duchess, is unfair to guests who undergo the strain of having their eyes "fixed on the ceiling." In informal surroundings a jocular comment from the honest perpetrator by way of both acknowledgement and apology is quite acceptable. "Whoops, I must get that fixed." No one is apt to argue.

A genteel parson who produces a NAND in Bible study class can deflect embarrassment by quickly quoting Numbers 11:31, "And there went forth a wind from the Lord," thereby suggesting that even the Almighty is afflicted. If the reverend has produced a NAD he may choose to observe that the Lord's wind knocked quail from the sky. This can lead into a devout theological discussion as to whether the Bible should be interpreted literally or metaphorically.

On social occasions, the more formal the setting the less chance there is for the producer to say something entirely appropriate. It is up to the host, or even the hostess, to use sympathetic verbal ingenuity and mock disapproval: "I thought you'd be presenting that report to the Board."

It would require a skillful hostess indeed to issue Queen Elizabeth's regal dictum that she had "forgot the fart," and still be able to make a guest feel at ease. The modern hostess might earn more accolades with casual critical appraisal, such as, "Not bad for a one-inch speaker," or, "The tone is true but the volume needs adjustment," or even, "Well modulated with intriguing harmonics." Such comments should be delivered as a congratulatory aside without interrupting the general flow of conversation.

If the explosive intrusion comes in the midst of an animated after dinner discussion the host might well field it with a direct question, "Is that personal opinion or editorial comment?" An appropriate response would be that it was a spontaneous remark springing from the pressure of inner conviction and not intended in any way to smother the opinions of others. In this merry way, embarrassment can be deflected by genteel wit. Shame can be transmuted to smiles by the alchemy of compassion.

Special sympathy and understanding can be extended to pregnant women who, because of ever increasing pressure upon the interior gas works, are apt to sound off at inopportune moments. Their freeps should be ignored but the trauma of a maternal thundergust can be softened by, "Supportive little chap, that — already he's tooting your horn."

Sarcasm is not recommended as a redemptive tool. It only works as a healing agent in a situation where the farteur is immune to sarcasm. Such was the case with a Sir Henry Englefield's conviction that his own vile emanations were scented. One day when he transgressed, Lady Grenville sarcastically exclaimed about the smell of violets. "Yes," said he, "It comes from me."[7]

Sir Henry's problem, of course, was not with the simple fart which tends to be noisily rowdy rather than silently noxious. His was the more complex variety, laden with volatiles. It was the kind we have classified as the slider (also known as the SAD).

The slider is a problem because it does not speak up to announce its point of origin. It is like an unsigned letter; it can be inflicted upon others without attribution (or retribution). Only a Sir Henry would admit to owning one. Paradoxically, this creates a situation where sensitive farteurs can be more overwhelmed with guilt than if they were to launch uproarious skillsaws.

oOo

Purgatives: Sulphur, salts and 'perpetual pills'

Since the slider is produced by rogue volatiles created by bacterial action it is difficult to attack it directly. Indeed, Benjamin Franklin suggested that diligent dietary research should be able to turn our odoriferous emanations into sweet perfume for then there would be no concern about suppression.[8] He was being facetious but it is a thought that modern research might follow up.

Some earlier generations were more convinced than is our own, that frequent irrigation of the interior piping was essential for health and happiness. It is possible, however, that their frequent flushing of the system might indeed have reduced the bacterial action thereby reducing the volatiles and inhibiting the production of sliders.

Flushing was carried out by a variety of means. Doting mothers cleaned their families on the outside with lye soap and on the inside with seasonal doses of sulphur and molasses. Epsom salts in lemonade made a convenient and swift purge. Detergent herbs disguised in figs created an edible cleanout cake that left entire generations with a healthy dislike of figs.

A story circulates that in the 19th century a metal, antimony, was molded into indigestible pills intended to travel the entire system cleaning it out en route. Being indestructible, the pills were said to be recoverable at the end of the journey. They were even supposed to be commonly known as "perpetual pills" because having passed through one generation they could be passed on to the next.

Most of such purported purgatives were thought by their practitioners to be ways of "cleansing the blood" and they may indeed have impeded unwanted bacterial action. Unfortunately for science, the human parade did not at that time include flatologists bringing up the rear collecting air samples.

An even more direct attack on bacterial buildup was popular in the 1800s in England. It was the voluntary enema (as opposed to the medically prescribed one). There were many exotic devices sold for the purpose of self-administering an enema most of which would make today's waterbag, hose and nozzle contraption look positively primitive. Some were built into commode seats so that the user could sit upon the injector and activate it with the stroke of a pump handle. (These contraptions are only rarely explained during present-day tours of old mansions and castles.) At one time in England the self-delivered enema became a fad indulged in by the well-to-do. Again, alas, there are no statistics to tell us whether they were therefore less flatulent than we.

The enema has not totally passed from the scene. At least one American doctor[9] even recommends the discreet self-administering of a mini-enema with a baby syringe prior to sexual activity. This may be useful advice for those who have difficulty avoiding the Swiftian blast or the Bandyian hiss that might put out Love's Fires.

oOo

Perils of inadvertant air gulping

Today's society is, perhaps incorrectly, less prone to use self-directed remedies and more likely to seek professional help. Here is where the doctor, the psychologist and the dietitian appropriately enter our discussion.

All clinicians warn against the excessive swallowing of air. Simply put, if we persist in manipulating our false teeth, chewing gum, smoking, talking with our mouths full, and so forth, we will undoubtedly burp, belch, and fart more than is necessary or even seemly. Concerned farteurs might well begin with a serious assessment of their own patterns of air intake. Air ingested becomes air expelled.

Swallowed air may result in more burping than farting but there are dissenting opinions. One comes from Dr. R. Hecker, Director of Gastroenterology at Australia's Royal Adelaide Hospital, who believes that "swallowed air is the commonest cause of excess flatus." He also states that it only takes 20 minutes for swallowed gases to go from the stomach to the colon.[10]

This figure is worth pondering. It means that any diner concerned about creating anti-social interjections might do well to eat carefully and leisurely. The price for talking with one's mouth full could well be an impromptu stint as an unwelcome after dinner speaker or – may St. Augustine save us – a 'singer.'

oOo

A healthy diet is a breezy diet

Most researchers feel that diet is the principal tool to be used in controlling the common fart. Indeed, in a report on flatulence in *The Annual Review of Medicine*, Levitt and Bond say that excessive farting "can most frequently be related to the composition of the diet and virtually never indicates serious organic disease of the gastrointestinal tract."[11]

(Thankfully we note that there is nothing in current scientific literature that gives support to the belief that flatulence is in itself life threatening. The Emperor Claudius, the doctors at Salerno, Montaigne and Robbie Burns to the contrary, death may be caused when the bowels are blocked by a tumour or other obstruction. Flatulence causes social discomfort, not death).

Certain foods are more flatulogenic than others, and some people may be more sensitive than others. Laying all the blame on a particular food or group of foods seems unfair when, in some cases, poor absorption,allergy, disease, or even a lack of water may be the culprit. Generally the more flatogenic foods are said to be high fibre grains, lactose containing foods such as milk and milk products, onions, beans, celery, carrots, raisins, bananas, apricots, prune juice and prunes, pretzels, bagels, wheat germ, brussel sprouts.[12] The list, however, can be extended to include broccoli, cabbage, cauliflower, kale, kohlrabi, rutabaga, turnips, and turnip greens.[13]

There is a case on record of a farteur who went through 130 foods before finding a diet that he, and presumably his friends, could live with.[14] Fortunately, most of us will find our personal list of problem foods to be more modest, and a little relief from our wilful wind can sometimes be achieved simply by rotating the foods that are a problem, or eating them in smaller quantities.

Even drinking more water can help. Without sufficient water intake, food takes longer to make its gastric journey giving it more time to create explosives. Some beverages, such as coffee and tea, can actually cause dehydration, but 6 to 8 glasses of water a day keep things moving.

A personal intolerance to lactose (the sugar found in milk products) can be an uncomfortable and noisy nuisance. A study was carried out many years ago on a patient who was already plagued by an average of 34 farts per day. When put on a pure milk diet the subject produced 141 emissions per day, achieving as many as 70 within one four-hour period for an average of one release every three-and-a-half minutes. Through diet modification alone the subject was able to reduce emissions to a mere sixteen per day, only a smidgen above the normal average of fourteen. [15]

For those who have difficulty digesting lactose (most prevalent in milk and cottage cheese) yogurt and aged cheese containing "far less lactose"[16] are pleasant alternatives that create far less thunder. It is prudent to remember, however, that yogurts containing "active culture" (lactobacillus) would be lowest in lactose. Fortunately these can be identified by a careful reading of the label and by the clear milky residue, the whey, that rises to the top of the product.

Legumes (all varieties of beans, peas and lentils) seem to contribute to the manufacture of intestinal gas. But each of these also varies in gas production capabilities. Dutch brown beans, for instance, have been found to be more gas productive than are peas.[17] At least two researchers take note of Jerusalem artichokes which contain an indigestible sugar known to produce "notorious effects."[18]

It was all very well for Pythagorus to warn his followers not to eat beans, but legumes are becoming a popular component of modern diets. They have a desirable protein value (especially in combination with grains), and contain many of the B vitamins, minerals, and fibre. However, beans are high in a poorly-tolerated form of carbohydrate (the oligo saccharides) contributing voluminously to the peak period for adult flatus production, which is usually about six hours after eating a bean meal. For children the peak period is between four and five hours after eating.[19] Forewarned may be fore-distanced.

This means, of course, that the post-bean episode in the film *Blazing Saddles,* coming as it did immediately after the meal, relied more on artistic license than on documentary fact. It also suggests that if one is attending a social event a simple preplanning of the day's diet can intercept and becalm the Vulgar Wind.

There are other flatus factors present in currently popular foods. The consumption of immodest amounts of artificial sweeteners, beloved by the makers of "sugar free" food, drink, and gum can cause not only farting but diarrhea.[20] It is one of life's little ironies that achieving the socially acceptable slim figure may also achieve the socially unacceptable acoustical improprieties.

High fibre diets are very popular and indeed are highly recommended. In Canada, a recent revision of the national food guide virtually doubled the suggested intake of grains, fruits and vegetables previously recommended for healthy eating.[21]

But some fibre-containing foods contribute to the conditions conducive to gas production. Consequently there is a social price to be paid for too sudden an infatuation with whole grain breads, bran cereals, legumes and even vegetables. *The operative word is "sudden." Gradual conversion to a high fibre diet will ease the danger to either social status or the environment.*

It would be folly to shun an otherwise healthy diet for fear of a little flatulence. A healthy diet can be a breezy diet.

Those of us who cherish our roughage and our health can take heart from Dr. Ted Boadway, Director of Health Policy for the Ontario Medical Association, who reassures us in a forthright fashion: "Farting is a fact of life, and you are an audible manifestation of a virtuous lifestyle."[22]

oOo

The inflationary FF Index

The implications of the fart as a dietary by-product have not yet been fully appreciated by the manufacturers of prepared foods. The time may come when, along with the ingredients, it will be mandatory to display a flatus factor,"FF Index," that will rate the particular food's gas producing potential on a scale of 0 to 10.

Merchandizers who are becoming sensitive to environmentally acceptable products should give some thought voluntarily to making their products socially benevolent as well. Among consumers who value proper etiquette, an "FF 0" could have as strong an appeal to the shopper as do today's "light," "lite" and "low calorie" labels.

No doubt there will also be consumers who, in an excess of exuberant impropriety, reach knowingly for the can or box bearing an FF 10 rating. Indeed, the FF 10 label could become a big seller among the Blue Angel elite class.*

Readers who find the idea of a mandatory flatus factor rating to be somewhat fart fetched might wish to consider that a plain and nourishing meal of great northern beans, whole wheat toast, orange juice and peaches, quite in keeping with modern dietary trends, was the very one chosen by researchers[23] wishing to give subjects a nourishing but highly gas forming meal.

In considering the foods we eat, there can be no question of shunning a healthy diet in order to suppress flatulence. Understanding the potential of various foods can help us modulate intake prior to those occasions when, for social reasons at least, we wish to becalm the wind.

oOo

Tampering with natural phenomena

Farteurs who are concerned because they feel they are overshooting normal daily limits should, of course, consult their doctor. Physical causes may be detected and treated. But lacking such causes doctors may experiment with changes in diet or even

—

*Since the Blue Angel, or methane capability, seems to run in families, one is tempted to speculate about the hazards of family get-togethers. Especially those in hot tubs, and most especially if there is a smoker present. Should the high numbered FF Index products carry a combustion warning?

prescribe tranquilizers to alleviate stress. With only a little reticence, we suggest that a prescription to read this small book might help the patient unwind and, more importantly, develop a friendlier relationship with the frolicsome fart.

In the event that the physician decides that diet alone will not remedy the problem, there are several drugs that are frequently prescribed. It seems somehow unsporting to attack the monosyllabic fart with, for example, "iodochlorhydroxyquin." Further, in the opinion of some flatologists,[24] these are of little use.

One prescription, however, that is gaining considerable attention is, paradoxically, an old one – activated charcoal. In 1830, Touey advocated charcoal as an antidote for strychnine poisoning. He went so far as to take a more-than-lethal dose of the poison along with a 15 gram dose of charcoal. He not only survived, but reported no unusual effects.[25]

Now, more than a century and a half later, activated charcoal is still being used as the antidote of choice for acute poisoning and also for counteracting a kind of social strychnine – the fart. Dosages used are quite low, are said to be without side-effects, and provide encouraging results.[26]

Flatologists are not unanimous in their admiration for charcoal as a human muffler but some claim that "the use of activated charcoal is a new and promising therapeutic alternative that awaits further critical analysis."[27] Since this statement in 1985, charcoal has continued to gain credibility. A popular book of home remedies recommends activated charcoal tablets as a fart fighter, but does warn us to check with our doctor if we're taking medicine. The charcoal may try to absorb it too![28]

For those optimists dedicated to the pursuit of a pill for every ill, there is always, instead, the cultural remedy: "Perhaps," says Dr. Grant Thompson of the University of Ottawa School of

Medicine, "increased tolerance of flatus would be a better solution, for we tamper with harmless natural phenomena at our peril."[29]

oOo

Studies in long term deflation

In the days when North American housewives bought their dried peas and beans in bulk and did all preparations at home, it was taken for granted that the pulses would be soaked overnight in cold water, then drained and brought to a boil in fresh water, eventually to be drained again and rinsed, covered yet again with fresh water, brought back to the boil and cooked to completion. This was the classic way to tenderize the legumes. More importantly, experience taught that it was also a good way to diminish the flatus factors.

A study conducted at the University of Jos, Nigeria, reduced the flatus factors in soya milk through hours of soaking the beans followed by draining, blanching, boiling, stirring, cooling, grinding, filtering and more boiling.[30] In India, a study of legumes showed that the flatus factors could also be reduced by means of an elaborate fermentation process used in making traditional Indonesian "tempeh."[31]

Such time-consuming processes are not likely to be popular in the fast food cultures of the developed world. Yet, as legumes (such as soya beans, the vegetarians' mainstay) gain popularity, it becomes socially imperative for us to be aware of the explosive potential of some inadequately prepared carbohydrates.

The reduction of the flatus factors in food is a little-publicized byproduct of the controversial method of food preservation known as irradiation. A passage in *The Western Journal of Medicine* speaks for itself:

The search for a cure of this noisy, malodorous malady takes us to Bombay, India, where V.S. Rao and U.K. Vakil, working at the Bhabba Atomic Research Centre (after all this is an explosive problem) are learning how to deflate the legumes that are a staple in the diet of Indians and of the people throughout the Third World. It's quite simple. After a preliminary soaking of the beans in distilled water they are then exposed to a minimum amount of cobalt-60 radiation. Result: the two main culprits in flatulence production, stachyose and raffinose, become digestible, thereby reducing the gaseous fermentation.*[32]

If bean irradiation with cobalt-60 ever gains widespread acceptance, the world will become a quieter and sweeter place.

The winds of change (vulgar and otherwise) however, continue to waft across the flatological landscape. New frontiers (or in this case, reartiers) are constantly being explored. Recently, an upstart opponent of the fart burst onto the North American scene making almost as rowdy an entry as its antagonist makes an exit. Some of its promotional press kits included a whoopee cushion. Even its name, "Beano," echoed the same kind of bravado and devil-may-care attitude that has graced (or disgraced) its adversary.

Beano is an activist. It does not wait around for a fart to form and then react. It deflates the culprit sugars before digestion takes place. In terms of flatological warfare it makes a preemptive strike by turning the indigestible sugars of complex carbohydrates into digestible non-gas-producing forms. Several drops squirted onto the first mouthful, is said to do the trick for the whole meal. Beano has also appeared in pill form.[33]

—

* This is the clinician's aside, not mine. Flatologists are as irrepressible as their subject.

Fortunately for the fart, Beano is not totally effective, for it makes no inroads against the milk-fed fart. So there is no need for the alarm voiced by a Canadian journalist – "How will small boys bond with their dads?"[34]

A jaunty upstart like Beano may have us teetering on the brink of a social revolution. It is possible that its regular use will become as much an obligatory ritual in polite society as the spreading of serviettes or the saying of grace.

But what of the few nonconformists who may have developed an affinity for the fart? Will such pervasive deflationary rituals send them complaining to human rights commissions?

oOo

A strange source of flatulence

The mind is yet another player not to be overlooked in our quest for understanding. It is not difficult to imagine a person having a fear of farting. Indeed, the cultural strictures of our society make such a fear almost obligatory. But that such a fear can become obsessive was amply demonstrated in a case reported by psychologists Michael A. Milan and David J. Kolko of Georgia State University.[35]

Milan and Kolko were confronted by a 33 year old woman who was so concerned about the frequency of what she perceived to be malodorous emissions that she was virtually withdrawing from all social interaction. Ms P., as they called her, was a well educated person and before seeking psychiatric help she had, over the course of 10 years, been treated by a variety of specialists attempting everything from dietary control, to gas analysis, relaxation skills and drug therapy.

They had all concluded that there was no physical justification for her obsessions and that, therefore, it must all be in her head. The reader can be pardoned for wondering if the head is not a strange place to produce flatulence and can no doubt sympathize with Ms P. who, following instructions from Milan and Kolko, kept a fartgraph that certainly provided undeflatable evidence that she was in the gas production business.

The two behaviourists then prescribed a treatment that is known as "paradoxical." They theorized that frequent minor emissions would prevent the buildup of gas and so, far from simply exhorting Ms P. not to worry about her flatulence, they encouraged her to fart upon the slightest provocation. Like flatalogical high priests they gave the supplicant dispensation from her perceived social sin.

Ms P. embraced the dispensation and was able to report an almost instant decline in the number and intensity of emissions. A one-year follow up showed that she had become a calm, socially relaxed person, enjoying the companionship of others, with no more tendency to fart than has any other normal person.

Paradoxical treatment, indeed. But then, as was noted in Chapter One, the fart is nothing if not paradoxical. It seems only fitting to dedicate a limerick to Ms P. and to her laid-back advisors:

A lady of gaseous fertility
Offered this soothing soliloquy,
"The more that I farted,
The urge it departed,
Resulting in peace and tranquility."

AFTWIND

It is obvious that the Vulgar Wind is a resilient and elusive subject, as reluctant to be terminated on paper as in life. Others will want to pick up the torch (being careful of Blue Angels) to carry on with a topic that is clamouring to be heard.

Indeed, the challenge was laid down a number of years ago by an eminent flatologist who called for the deflation of mythology, bemoaned our befogged state of understanding, and called for data to be pumped into a field filled largely with hot air. He prophesied that "intestinal gas will then become the rightful province of both flatologists and scatologists."[1]

oOo

The journey to deflate and disperse

To deflate mythology and to disperse some fog, but to do so with gentility, has been the serious intent in this work. The scatology we have left to others.

We have journeyed through history and literature , through medicine and nutrition, and have reassured ourselves that there is nothing new, innovative, unique, exclusive, or even innately degrading, about the Vulgar Wind.

It is a universal essence of life itself and nothing about it is inherently life or health threatening even though it may cause mental anguish, social discomfort and not a little embarassment. By describing what it really is – a modest and natural waste product of the amazing human body – we have tried to alter some perceptions of the common fart.

We have also attempted to shed some light (cautiously so as

not to incur explosions) on the many gases that are produced in the digestive process, why they are produced and even how. But anyone searching for polysyllabic detail on the mysteries of the digestive tract must look elsewhere.

oOo

Only two ways to go

When dealing with flatulence, there are really only two ways to go. Firstly, to attempt to reduce emissions and secondly, to learn to live with those that stubbornly remain behind. Total elimination is not in the cards. Or in Nature.

There are several paths we can follow to reach these two complementary goals and they have been examined in order to provide us with an extended vocabulary, some historic precedence, scientific and literary sources and even some genteel excuses should the need arise.

Denial: We found that denial is acceptable if we simply mean ignoring the presence of a modest freep. But even in a supposedly liberated society the requirement to ignore a cannonade is asking too much. Denial is also unacceptable if one attempts in any way to shift personal responsibility.

Dialogue: We found that dialogue, if non-acrimonious, relaxed, and cheerful, was much better than denial, especially when something like a flutterblast clamours for attention at a social gathering. We saw that the word "fart" had a long and honourable history but had been suppressed by the culture of denial. There is room for a broader vocabulary to encourage and enhance discreet dialogue, and we have proffered some suggestions.

Detergency: This refers to the flushing out (by one means or another) of the digestive tract, a practice more popular with our ancestors than it is with us. It may, however, have helped to reduce rogue volatiles like hydrogen sulphide, which have been largely responsible for the lowly reputation of the slider.

Deportment: In excessive amounts, air gulping was found to be another culprit contributing to air expulsion. Simply put, manipulating our false teeth, smoking, chewing gum, talking with our mouths full, and so forth, results in burps, belches, and farting more than is necessary or even seemly.

Diet: Here is an important key to control. Certain foods are more flatulogenic than others. Personal experimentation (and the sincere advice of those close to us) may discern which foods to shun altogether and which to avoid several hours before a social event. If one wishes to shift to a modern high fibre, largely vegetarian diet, one should do so gradually so the digestive system can adapt. Ample water intake is always beneficial.

The fart is an intrinsic byproduct of a healthy diet and good health requires that we accept and recognize it as a breezy companion, not a blustery foe.

Drugs: Drugs do not have a good track record in subduing the fart. Some clinicians approve of activated charcoal as an anti-flatulent although even here opinion waffles. Advice from our physician is recommended.

Deflation: Removal of flatus factors from food involves the careful preparation of those foods known to be flatulogenic. Some time honoured methods of preparing pulses do prove somewhat deflationary but are time consuming. Irradiation by

Cobalt-60 reduces flatus factors but is unlikely to become popular. A food enzyme marketed under the impudent name of Beano shows promise as a deflationary agent.

Dispensation: The granting of permission to do what is usually forbidden has much to recommend it and such 'dispensation' can be conferred by ourselves, our peers, or our psychiatrists. Since the very fear of farting creates stress and stress promotes flatulence, permission to unleash the turbulent wind can, paradoxically, calm it. Dispensation and Dialogue are good companions.

oOo

Farteurs all

No attempts to prevent or suppress will ever completely eliminate the fart. It is a much maligned natural byproduct of absolutely essential organic functions. Therefore it seems logical that in addition to taking normal precautions, we loosen not the sphincter, but the cultural mores and conversational taboos surrounding the Vulgar Wind.

After all, the real meaning of the word "vulgar" does not pertain to objectionable coarseness, but to 'being of the masses.' And flatulence is indisputably and universally of 'the masses.' Whether we produce sliders, calicoes, skillsaws, freeps, flams, ruffs, paradiddles, mommadaddies, mud-ducks, flutterblasts, fundusbreaks, NADs, NANDs or SADs, and whether we like it or not, we are farteurs all.

NOTES

FOREWIND

1. Brody, J. *The New York Times Guide to Personal Health.* Times Books: N.Y. 1982. Pages 533, 536. © Random House Inc. N.Y.

2. Boadway, T. "As Diets Change, So Should the Old Social Taboo." *The Toronto Star* 26 November 1991. Final Edition Opinion. Page A17.

3. Palmer, E.D. The Colonic Gas Problem. *American Family Physician* February 1978 Editorial. Volume 17, Number 2. Pages 92-5.

4. Bond, J.H. and Levitt, M.D. "Gaseousness and Intestinal Gas." *Medical Clinics of North America* January 1978. Volume 62, Number 1. Pages 155-64.

5. Levitt, M.D. "Intestinal Gas Production – Recent Advances in Flatology." *The New England Journal of Medicine* 26 June 1980. Volume 302, Number 26. Pages 1474-5.

6. Levitt, M.D. and Bond, J.H. "Flatulence." *Annual Review of Medicine* 1980. Volume 31. Pages 127-37.

CHAPTER ONE: THE OUTCAST

1. Dick, O.L. (Editor) *Aubrey's Brief Lives.* Martin Secker & Warburg Ltd.:London. 1941.

2. Hecker, R. "Indigestion and Flatulence." *Australian Family Physician* June 1981. Volume 10, Number 6. Pages 447-451.

3. Van Ness, M.M. and others. "Flatulence: Pathophysiology and Treatment." *American Family Physician* April 1985. Volume 31, Number 4. Pages 198-208.

4. Levitt, M.D. 1980.

5. Altman D.F. "Downwind Update – a Discourse On Matters Gaseous." *The Western Journal of Medicine* October 1868. Volume 145, Number 4. Pages 502-505.

6. Watson, W.C. "Speaking the Unspeakable." *New England Journal of Medicine* August 1978. Volume 299, Number 9. Page 494.

7. Read, N.W. "Mechanisms of Flatulence and Diarrhoea [sic]." *British Journal of Surgery* September 1985. Volume 72 Supplement. Pages s5-s6.

8. Altman, D.F. 1868.

9. Essop, A.R. and Segal, I. "Air-flow Studies in Excessive Flatulence." *The Practitioner* (U.K.) April 1983. Volume 227. Page 647.

10. Fox, E.R.W. "Maizie's Problem." *The Western Journal of Medicine* September 1985. Volume 143, Number 3. Page 401.

CHAPTER TWO: WHY THE WIND BLOWS

1. Health and Welfare Canada. "Nutrition Recommendations. *The Report of the Scientific Review Committee 1990.*

2. Levitt, M.D. and Bond, J.H. 1980.

3. Hecker, R. 1981.

4. Van Ness, M.M. and others. 1985

5. Levitt, M. D. and Bond, J.H. 1980

6. Van Ness, M.M. and others. 1985.

7. Aurbach, P. and Miller, Y.E. High Altitude Flatus Expulsion (HAFE). *The Western Journal of Medicine* February 1983. Volume 134. Pages 173-74.

8. Levy, E.I. "Explosions During Lower Bowel Electrosurgery." *American Journal of Surgery* 1954. Volume 88. Page 754.

9. The reader who wishes a more comprehensive and technically accurate explanation of the physiology of intestinal gas will find a list of references following Levitt, M.D. and Bond. J. H. 1980.

10. Levitt,M.D. and Bond, J.H.1980.

CHAPTER THREE: WHERE THE WIND HAS BLOWN

1. Levitt, M.D. and Bond, J.H. 1980.

2. Fox, E.R.W. "Maizie's Problem." 1985.

3. Bouchier, I.A.D. "Flatulence." *The Practitioner* (U.K.) April 1980. Volume 224. Pages 373-7.

4. *The Medical Works of Hippocrates.* Translated by J. Chadwick and W.N. Mann. Blackwell Scientific Publications: Oxford. 1950. Pages 118, 262.

5. Gaius Suetonius Tranquillus. *The Twelve Caesars.* Translated by R. Graves. Cassell & Company Ltd.: London. (no date given) © A.P. Watt Ltd. on behalf of the Trustees of the Robert Graves Copyright Trust.

6. St. Augustine. *The City of God.* Translated by J. Healey and revised by Rev. R.V.G. Tasker.Everyman's Library: London 1945. Book XIV Chapter XXIV. Page 55. © David Campbell Publishers Ltd.

7. Whiting, B.J., Millett, F.B. and others. *The College Survey of English Literature.* Harcourt Brace & Company: New York 1945. Page 99. (It may be of passing interest to note that this magnificent tome does not expose students to Chaucer's raunchy Miller's Tale from the Canterbury saga.)

8. Chaucer, G. *The Canterbury Tales.* Translated by N. Coghill. Penguin Classics. 4th Revised Edition. 1977. © Penguin Books: London.

9. Skeat, W.W. (Editor) The Milleres [sic] Tale. *The Canterbury Tales* Complete and Unabridged. Random House Modern Library: N.Y. 1957. Page 93. Lines 96-7.

10. Chaucer, G. 1977. 4th Revised Edition.

11. Rabelais, F. *The Works of Rabelais.* Illustrated by G. Dore. Chatto & Windus: London. (no date given) Book 1, Chapter XIII.
12. De Montaigne, E. M. "Of the Power of the Imagination." Excerpted from *The Complete Essays of Montaigne.* Translated by D. M. Frame. Stanford University Press. 1958. Book I, Chapter XXI. Page 73. © 1958 by the Board of the Trustees of the Leland Stanford Junior University.
13. De Montaigne, E.M. 1958.
14. Swift, J. *A Treatise on Good Manners and Good Breeding.* In Grolier's Harvard Classics: English Essays. Grolier Inc.: Connecticut. 1969. 62nd Printing.
15. Murray, J.M. *Jonathan Swift: A Critical Biography.* Jonathan Cape: London. 1954.
16. *Works of the Rev Jonathan Swift, D.D.* Nichols & Son: London. 1801. Volume 8 of 19 Volumes. Pages 101-110.
17. Ash, R. and Lake, B. (Editors). *Frog Raising for Pleasure and Profit and Other Bizarre Books.* Macmillan London Ltd.: London. 1985. Page 64. The accolade is from the publication which features unusual titles. In addition to the Swiftian effort there are Suggestive Thoughts for Busy Workers, published by The Bible Christian Book Room, 1883; Proceedings of the Second International Workshop on Nude Mice, University of Tokyo Press, 1978 – and much worse.
18. Ash, R. and Lake, B. 1985.
19. de Balzac, H. *Journal des Goncourts.* (1855) Translated by L. Galantiere. Doubleday & Co.: N.Y. 1958. © Bantam doubleday Dell, N.Y.
20. Twain, M. *Mark Twain's Conversation As It Was by the Social Fireside in the Time of the Tudors.* Embellished with an Illuminating Introduction, Facetious Footnotes and a Bibliography by Franklin J. Meine. Privately printed for the Mark Twain Society of Chicago. 1939.
21. Twain, M. 1939.
22. Ramsay, R. and Emberson, F. G. *A Mark Twain Lexicon.* Russell & Russell Inc.: N.Y. 1963.
23. Ramsay, R. and Emberson, F.G. 1963.
24. For this and the following Pujol references, see Nohain, J. and Caradec, F. *Le Petomane.* Bell Publishing Co.: N.Y. 1985. © Souvenir Press: London.
25. Nohain, J. and Caradec, F. 1985 quoting Dr. Marcel Baudoin from *La Semaine Medicale* 1892.
26. Townsend, Peter. *Time and Chance: An Autobiography.* HarperCollins: London.
27. The Peter Pauper Press. *The World's Best Limericks.* The Peter Pauper Press: Mt. Vernon, N.Y. 1978. Page 49. This limerick is unusual in that it can be quoted for readers who have not lost all sense of verbal propriety. Most limericks that take their inspiration from the gastrointestinal tract are execrably excremental, which

is too bad because the limerick is a charming device. Those that appear later on in this book are written by me in a hopeful attempt to elevate the limerick along with the fart. This confession also applies to the footnote on page 3.
28. Mills, John. *Up in the Clouds, Gentlemen Please.* Weidenfeld & Nicolson: London. 1980.
29. Jack, D. *Me too (The Bandy Papers).* Doubleday: Toronto & N.Y. 1983. Pages 236-7.
30. Layton, I. To the Priest Who Kept My Wife Awake All Night, Farting. *Nail Polish.* McClelland & Stewart, The Canadian Publishers: Toronto. 1971.

CHAPTER FOUR: THE WIND AND THE WORDS

1. Wentworth, H. and Flexner, S. B. (Editors) *Dictionary of American Slang.* Thomas Y. Crowell & Co.: N.Y. 1967. See the Preface.
2. Berkow, R. (Editor-in-Chief) *The Merck Manual of Diagnosis and Therapy.* Merck & Co. West Point, PA. 16th Edition, 1992.
3. For more than you probably want to know about drum beats, consult Sadie, S. (Editor) *The New Grove Dictionary of Music and Musicians* Macmillan Ltd. 1980. Page 645.
4. Wetzel, D. *Joel's Journal and Fact-Filled Fart Book.* Planet Books: N.Y. 1983.
5. Canadian Broadcasting Corporation (CBC) "The Crepitation Contest." Circa 1946.

CHAPTER FIVE: GOING WITH THE WIND

1. Levitt, M.D. and Bond, J.H. 1980.
2. Interview on the CBC radio network's Quirks and Quarks with scientist Florentin Krause, from the Lawrence Berkeley Laboratory at Berkeley California. January 20, 1990.
3. Siegel, L. "Did Global Warming Start with Puff the Methane Dinosaur?" *The Toronto Star* 26 October 1991.
4. Anti-odour Ordinance Cover Gas? *The Lawyer's Weekly* (Butterworth) 24 July 1992. Volume 12, Number 13. Page 2.
5. Martin, J. *Miss Manner's Guide to Excruciatingly Correct Behavior.* Atheneum Publishers: N.Y. 1982.
6. Martin, J. 1982.
7. *Table Talk of Samuel Rogers.* (1856) As quoted in F. Muir's *An Irreverant and Almost Complete Social History of the Bathroom.* Wm. Heinnemann Ltd.: London 1982. Pages 98-101.
8. Franklin, B. *Steven Collection of Franklin Manuscripts.* State Department, Washington, D.C.
9. Dr. Gerald M. Feigen from Mount Zion Hospital, San Francisco. As quoted in Brody, J. 1982.

10. Hecker, R. 1981.
11. Levitt, M. D. and Bond, J. H. 1980.
12. Van Ness, M. M. and others 1985.
13. Brody, J. *Jane Brody's Good Food Book.* Bantam: N.Y. 1987.
14. Levitt, M D., Lasser, R. B. and others. "Studies of a Flatulent Patient." *New England Journal of Medicine* 1976. Volume 295. Pages 260-2.
15. Levitt, M.D., Lasser, R.B. and others. 1976.
16. Brostoff, J. and Gamin, L. *The Complete Guide to Food Allergy and Intolerance.* Bloomsbury Publishing: London. 1989. Page 202.
17. Geervani, P and Theophilus, F. "Flatus Inducing Effects of Processed Legumes in Pre-School Children." *Indian Journal of Medical Research.* November 1979. Volume 70. Pages 750-5.
18. Brostoff, J. and Gamin, L. 1989. Page 115.
19. Geervani, P. and Theophilus, F. 1979.
20. "Downwind with Bulk Sweeteners." *Drug and Therapeutics Bulletin* 30 December 1983. Volume 21, Number 26. Page 104. See also: Oberrieder, H.K. and Fryer, E B. "College Student's Knowledge and Consumption of Sorbitol." *Journal of the American Dietetic Association* June 1991. Volume 91, Number 6. Pages 715-17.
21. Health and Welfare Canada. *Canada's Food Guide to Healthy Eating.* Revised 1992.
22. Boadway, T. 1991.
23. Hall, R.J. Jr., Thompson, H. and others. "Effects of Orally Administered Activated Charcoal on Intestinal Gas." *American Journal of Gastroenterology* March 1981. Volume 75, Number 3. Pages 192-6.
24. Van Ness, M.M. 1985.
25. Van Ness, M.M. 1985.
26. Van Ness, M.M. 1985. See also Hall, R., Thompson, J. and others 1981.
27. Van Ness, M.M. 1985.
28. Tkac, D. (Editor). *The Doctor's Book of Home Remedies.* Rodale Press: PA 1990. Page 270.
29. Thompson, W. G. "Additional Comments on Gastrointestinal Gas." *Canadian Medical Association Journal* 15 December 1988. Volume 139. Page 1141.
30. Kay, T. "Elimination of Flatus Factors in Soya Bean Preparation for a Rural Community." *Indian Journal of Experimental Biology.* June 1980. Volume 18, Number 6. Pages 658-9.
31. Kay, T., Jha, K. and Verma, J. "Removal of Flatus Principals from Legumes by Mold Fermentation." *Indian Journal Of Experimental Biology* June 1980. Volume 18, Number 6. Pages 658-9.
32. Fox, E.R.W. 1985.
33. Beano is the registered trademark of AkPharma Inc., Pleasantville, NJ

34. Trickey, M. "Product Takes the Bite out of Burps." *The Toronto Star* 16 February 1992. Page A16.
35. Milan, M. A. and Kolko, D.J. "Paradoxical Intention in the Treatment of Obsessional Flatulence Ruminations." *Journal of Behaviour Therapy and Experimental Psychiatry* June 1982. Volume 13, Number 2. Pages 167-72.

AFTWIND
1. Levitt, M. D. 1980.

Grateful acknowledgement is made for permission to reprint quotes and/or information from the following:

Brody, J. *The New York Times Guide to Personal Health.* © 1982 Random House Inc. New York.

Boadway, T. "As Diets Change, So Should the Old Social Taboo." © 1991 T. Boadway.

Palmer, E.D.The Colonic Gas Problem. © 1978 *American Family Physician*

Bond, J.H.and Levitt, M.D. "Gaseousness and Intestinal Gas." © 1978 *Medical Clinics of North America*

Levitt, M.D. "Intestinal Gas Production – Recent Advances in Flatology." © 1980 *The New England Journal of Medicine*

Levitt, M.D. and Bond, J.H. "Flatulence." © 1980 *Annual Review of Medicine*

Dick, O.L. (Editor) *Aubrey's Brief Lives.* © 1941 Martin Secker & Warburg Ltd.:London. By permission of Reed Book Services Ltd., a member of the Reed Elsevier group)

Hecker, R. "Indigestion and Flatulence." © 1981 *Australian Family Physician*

Van Ness, M.M. and others. "Flatulence: Pathophysiology and Treatment." © 1985 *American Family Physician*

Altman D.F."Downwind Update – a Discourse On Matters Gaseous." © 1868. *The Western Journal of Medicine*

Watson, W.C. "Speaking the Unspeakable.© 1978 *New England Journal of Medicine*

Essop, A.R. and Segal, I. "Air-flow Studies in Excessive Flatulence." © 1983 *The Practitioner* (U.K.)

Fox, E.R.W. "Maizie's Problem." © 1985 *The Western Journal of Medicine*

Bouchier, I.A.D. "Flatulence." © 1980 *The Practitioner* (U.K.)

The Medical Works of Hippocrates. Translated by J. Chadwick and W.N. Mann. © 1950 Blackwell Scientific Publications: Oxford.

St. Augustine. *The City of God.* Translated by J. Healey and revised by Rev. R.V.G. Tasker. © 1945 Everyman's Library: London.

Chaucer, G. *The Canterbury Tales.* Translated by N. Coghill. Penguin Classics. 4th Revised Edition.1977.© Neville Coghill 1951, 1958, 1960, 1975, 1977.

De Montaigne, E. M. "Of the Power of the Imagination." Excerpted from *The Complete Essays of Montaigne.* Translated by D. M.Frame, with permission of the publishers Stanford University Press. © 1958 by the Board of Trustees of the Leland Stanford Junior University.

Ash, R. and Lake, B. (Editors). *Frog Raising for Pleasure and Profit and Other Bizarre Books.* © 1985 Macmillan London Ltd.: London.

de Balzac, H. *Journal des Goncourts.* (1855) Translated by L. Galantiere.
© 1958 Bantam, Doubleday, Dell, New York.

Twain, M. *Mark Twain's Conversation As It Was by the Social Fireside in the Time of the Tudors.* Embellished with an Illuminating Introduction, Facetious Footnotes and a Bibliography by Franklin J. Meine. Privately printed for the Mark Twain Society of Chicago. 1939.

Nohain, J. and Caradec, F. *Le Petomane.* Bell Publishing Co.: N.Y. 1985.
© Souvenir Press, London.

Townsend, Peter. *Time and Chance: An Autobiography.*Harper Collins: London
© Collins, an imprint of Harpercollins Publishers Ltd. London.

The Peter Pauper Press *The World's Best Limericks.*
© 1978 The Peter Pauper PressVernon, N.Y..

Mills, John. *Up in the Clouds, Gentlemen Please.*
© 1980 Weidenfeld & Nicolson: London.

Jack, D. *Me too (The Bandy Papers).* Doubleday: Toronto & N.Y. © 1983. D. Jack.

Layton, I. "To the Priest Who Kept My Wife Awake All Night, Farting."
Nail Polish. © 1971 by McClelland & Stewart The Canadian Publishers, Toronto.

Berkow, R. (Editor-in-Chief) *The Merck Manual of Diagnosis and Therapy.*
16th Edition © 1992 Merck & Co. West Point, PA.

Wetzel, D. *Joel's Journal and Fact-Filled Fart Book.* Planet Books: N.Y.
© 1983 by D. Wetzel.

Canadian Broadcasting Corporation (CBC) *The Crepitation Contest.* Circa 1946.

Anti-odour Ordinance Cover Gas? © 1992 *The Lawyer's Weekly* (Butterworth Press)

Martin, J. *Miss Manner's Guide to Excruciatingly Correct Behavior.*Atheneum Publishers: N.Y..© 1982 Macmillan Publishing Co. London..

Table Talk of Samuel Rogers. (1856) As cited in F. Muir's *An Irreverant and Almost Complete Social History of the Bathroom.* Wm. Heinnemann Ltd.: London 1982.

Levitt, M D., Lasser, R. B. and others. "Studies of a Flatulent Patient."
© 1976 *New England Journal of Medicine*

Thompson, W. G. "Additional Comments on Gastrointestinal Gas."
© 1988 *Canadian Medical Association Journal*

Beano® With kind permission from AkPharma Inc., Pleasantville, NJ
Beano is a registered trademark of AkPharma Inc.

Trickey, M. "Product Takes the Bite out of Burps." © 1992 M. Trickey.

Milan, M. A. and Kolko, D.J. "Paradoxical Intention in the Treatment of Obsessional Flatulence Ruminations." © 1982 *Journal of Behaviour Therapy and Experimental Psychiatry*